MW00615096

# A Life    Interrupted

## The Long Night of Marjorie Day

Ruth Levy Guyer

ISBN: 978-0-615-60066-6

Printed at
Politics & Prose Bookstore
Washington, DC
www.politics-prose.com

In memory of Majorie Cornelia Day,
"Daysey,"
who wanted people to know her story


and


In memory of my parents,
Jean and Herbert Levy,
who would have loved to know what
actually happened

# Contents

## Prologue
## The Story of a Lifetime

What first drew me to Marjorie Cornelia Day's extraordinary story was a bare-bones, dramatic account of her experience that my neighbor, Emily, told me in 1977. Emily and I were drinking tea in her home, and I was telling her about a curious case history that I had been researching at work. At the time I was a medical writer at the National Institutes of Health. When I wrapped up my story, Emily said, "Have you ever encountered a case like this one?" and she launched into her astonishing tale.

Her friend, Marjorie Cornelia Day, called "Daysey" by her friends, had gone to England in 1925 to study philosophy and psychology at Oxford University. Only the rare woman was doing graduate work at Oxford in those days or, for that matter, anywhere, Emily said, but Daysey had been an anachronism throughout her life—usually ahead of her times—but, for one dreadful period, way behind it.

1

Daysey's misfortunes began during her spring break in 1926, when she and a number of her friends traveled down to Penzance on the southwestern coast of England for a study vacation. There, at the seaside, Daysey started to feel edgy, peculiar. She quickly grew worse, and, within days, she had lapsed into a coma.

Her startling descent into illness and unconsciousness frightened her friends and baffled the doctors who examined her. Daysey's parents were alerted, and her father, an American physician, sailed immediately to England, only to find his formerly lively and brilliant daughter insensate and unresponsive. He could do nothing but move her back to the States and install her in a hospital, where she remained pretty much a vegetable for the next seventeen years. Then for dramatic effect, Emily solemnly bobbed her head up and down and repeated slowly, "yes, seventeen years."

Then Emily fast forwarded to 1943. Daysey was still prone and silent. Her condition had not changed; the psychiatric hospital had become her permanent home. Early one afternoon, two nursing students came into Daysey's room to change the linens on her bed. The nurses were crisping the corners of Daysey's sheets and chatting about the psychology exam

2

they had taken earlier in the day.

"How did you answer that question about Freud's notion of _____ ?" one of the nurses asked the other. And, as the second nurse explained her 'take' on Freud, Daysey suddenly opened her eyes and said, "That's not at all what Freud meant" and proceeded to give a lucid account of Freud's point of view.

The dumb-struck nurses raced out of the room and drew in other members of the hospital staff. Daysey was holding forth on Freud, and she knew exactly what she was talking about. She was speaking, almost lecturing, and making complete sense. After seventeen years as a zombie, Daysey was suddenly absolutely clear, articulate, and so on target that one would have thought she had just then finished an in-depth, critical analysis of *The Ego and the Id*.

Daysey's sister, Marion, was summoned. Their father was no longer alive, and Marion was by then Daysey's legal guardian. Marion was absolutely thrilled to find her sister back among the living. And, as the weeks went by and Marion saw that Daysey's revivification was holding, she began to imagine a life for her sister outside the hospital.

But would Daysey be able to cope with the wider world? Marion started running some simple tests, taking Daysey out on short forays into the community. One evening at a restaurant, as the waiter poured ice water into the sisters' glasses, Daysey marveled that someone had "taken the time to carve those little cubes out of the ice block." Daysey had missed the moment when the ice man had stopped coming to every American home, and refrigerators with their ice trays had supplanted him. More significantly, Emily said, Daysey had slept through the Great Depression, the beginning of World War II, and so much more.

Eventually, Marion decided the time had come to spring Daysey from the hospital. She moved Daysey to Manhattan, where Daysey, Marion, and Marion's husband, Arnold, lived together in a midtown apartment.

For the next three years, Daysey walked each day from their communal family apartment to the New York Public Library. There, she sat in the periodical room and read the New York Times, starting from when she and the world parted company in 1926 until her reentry in 1943. In her library carrel, she would record in her meticulous Palmer Method script everything from the papers that captured her interest. She kept a set of notebooks—one for the arts, one for politics, one for economics, one for scientific discoveries—and that was how she caught up with a world that had played forward for seventeen years while she, herself, had remained on pause.

During one of Daysey's daily walks along Fifth Avenue, as she was heading home from the library in the vanishing sunlight late on a chill autumn afternoon, she saw a woman coming toward her who looked familiar. The woman spotted Daysey too, put her hand on her mouth in astonishment, and said, "Daysey! I thought you died!"

The woman was Daysey's favorite psychology professor and also the headmistress of a girls' preparatory school in New England where, after college, Daysey had taught Latin for several years before heading off to Oxford. Daysey and her professor—Emily didn't know her name, but I later learned it was Helen Temple Cooke—hugged and cried and talked, both completely overcome to see one another.

"I always wanted to teach, to be just like you," Daysey said, as she and Miss Cooke talked. But, surely now, that dream could not be realized, because what employer would overlook the seventeen-year gap in her resume, with its stigmatizing psychiatric hospitalization?

"But you can teach for me!" Miss Cooke

said without hesitation, right there on the sidewalk. She was still the headmistress of that prep school where Daysey had taught, and she hired Daysey on the spot to be a Latin teacher for the upcoming semester.

Thus was Daysey's teaching career summarily resurrected.

When, three years later, Daysey moved on from the prep school in New England to Mount Vernon College in Washington, D. C., she and Emily met and became colleagues and friends. Daysey was, according to Emily, the most popular teacher on campus.

A zombie for seventeen years.

A dramatic, spontaneous re-awakening with all of her intellectual faculties intact, including knowledge of Freudian theory and the ability to read and speak Latin.

A long life as a beloved college professor.

No. I had never before encountered a medical case history quite like that one.

Emily's account of Daysey's resurrection was, in fact, the most intriguing medical story I'd ever heard. What could possibly have caused Daysey's brain cells to lie dormant for 6000 days, then suddenly fire up again, and function fine?

I had just been reading Oliver Sacks's

book, *The Man Who Mistook His Wife for a Hat*, when Emily told me about Daysey. Sacks's clinical tales of curious case histories detail dysfunctions in the brains of his patients. Each story tells of an idiosyncratic deficit and also provides an interesting insight into how the healthy brain typically works. At times while reading Sacks's stories, I would envision the human brain as a succulent pie, with each patient's damaged brain missing a single, yet crucial, slice. Sometimes I considered a second image: that the brain was a roiling soup of sloshing chemicals and firing electrical signals. What a miracle it was that any two brains, whether pies or soups, could actually communicate with one another. And Daysey's brain had yet another fantastic feature to consider: it had emerged from a seventeen-year time warp apparently unscathed.

So, when I stood up from my tea with Emily, I was not just fired up by the story but actually primed to investigate it. I walked straight out of Emily's front door and directly over to the library at the National Institutes of Health, where I ran a search of the literature on the human brain and its pathologies.

Human physiology had intrigued me ever since my high school days, though my own college and graduate research had focussed on the immune system, not the brain. When I left the bench to become a medical writer, I learned that discoveries based on carefully controlled clinical trials and experiments like the ones I had done were not the only valid sources of information; much could also be gleaned from anecdotal information that came from unusual disease narratives of individual patients—what researchers call "the N of 1." Daysey was clearly an amazing N of 1.

Emily's account of Daysey's story— dramatic, engaging, although, as I later learned, not strictly accurate in every detail—set me on an obsessive path of investigation. I read every report I could find about cutting-edge advances in psychiatry and neurobiology, every published memoir by a person who had suffered a brain injury, and hundreds of clinical reports by physicians whose patients had experienced brain damage through injury or pathology. I combed the literature on the cellular and molecular biology of brain tissue. I followed up on each of the occasional stories that popped up in the news about someone who woke up after a lengthy coma.

But no story was quite like Daysey's story. Not one of the brain-damaged or resurrected individuals morphed from a vegetable to a high-functioning intellectual; more typically, those other 'awakenings' were short-lived and incomplete.

Emily had mentioned that Daysey's doctors considered, but then dismissed, two possibilities: first, that she might have somehow contracted African sleeping sickness, and, second, that she might have developed encephalitis after a bout with the flu.

When I looked into the signs, symptoms, and natural histories of African sleeping sickness and encephalitis, neither one made complete diagnostic sense to me either. The typical victim of the tsetse fly, for example, which is the organism that transmits African sleeping sickness from person to person, is a honey gatherer or a fisherman in sub-Saharan Africa, not an Oxford graduate student. And, even supposing that the renegade tsetse fly had made its way to Oxford or Penzance in a warm ship compartment or as part of some infectious disease researcher's collection, the natural course of African sleeping sickness begins with aches and fevers, then moves on to crushing lethargy, then a deep sleep, coma, and death. No resurrections have ever been documented.

Encephalitis, too, and even the form of

encephalitis that seemed the most likely to me — the one called encephalitis lethargica or "sleepy sickness" — was largely a death sentence in the 1920s and not something from which the occasional surviving victim ever fully recovered.

I kept thinking about Daysey, mulling over the story that Emily told me. I told my friends about Daysey; I told my colleagues, my students, and people I met at parties — and maybe one or two on trains. No one ever matched the tale with anything remotely comparable. Daysey's spontaneous, mysterious, and total revivification was apparently unique.

One night, many years after Emily first told me the story, I happened to be watching the local evening news, and, lo and behold, there was Daysey on my television screen, in my own den, talking to a reporter who was doing a series of Rip Van Winkle stories. Daysey was puffing on her pipe and saying that she intended to live to be 120, because she figured she was "owed" those extra years. She was absolutely captivating, smart, and charming, just as Emily had described her.

But, even after watching that interview, I still made no effort to meet Daysey. Today, I marvel that I hadn't simply said to Emily "Take me to Daysey!" after she told me the story, rather

than racing over to the library. I could argue that, while I was pondering Daysey's prolonged period of lethargy, some of her sluggishness had rubbed off on me. But, in fact, I had not been slouchy at all but intensely active in my pursuit of Daysey's story, just narrow minded. I was clearly much too slowly evolving from bench scientist—where the locus of action was in the laboratory—to medical writer—where I mistakenly thought everything happened in the library stacks. Years went by before I fully grasped that the N of 1 medical stories required actual personal encounters.

Finally, in 1991, fourteen years after Emily first told me about Daysey, I came to my senses. Late in August on a sticky, hot Washington afternoon, I strolled across the street and knocked on Emily's door.

"Emily," I said, "you've got to introduce me to Daysey."

Emily was somewhat hesitant to agree to the introduction. It was not going to be easy, she said. Daysey was 98 years old, and although she had all of her marbles, she was stone deaf. So, talking to her was complicated. You had to write down whatever you wanted to say on a note pad that Daysey kept at her side. Then she read what you wrote, and she'd start talking. The process, Emily said, could be quite tedious.

Eventually, though, Emily capitulated and arranged with Daysey for the three of us to meet. Emily suggested that I bring 'an offering,' some of my favorite books, because Daysey was a voracious reader.

I assembled my top-ten books—Sack's book was in the pile, as were Annie Dillard's *The Writing Life*, John McPhee's *Control of Nature*, Richard Selzer's *Imagine a Woman*, Laurie Colwin's *Goodbye Without Leaving*, Susan

Sontag's *AIDS and Its Metaphors*, and a few others — and I began formulating questions for the interview. I wanted to know what Daysey recalled, if anything, about her seventeen-year absence. I wanted to hear her account of that serendipitous Fifth Avenue encounter with her college professor, the prep school administrator. I wanted to know if she had ever learned anything definitive about what it was that had made her sick. And what was that Freudian 'slap' all about, the conversation between the two nurses that had so dramatically roused her from her years of coma and plunked her back down among the living with her brain intact? I was eager to hear what retrospective thoughts she had about her crazy fate during the many years of 'normal' living she had enjoyed after her resurrection.

On a grey September day in 1991, I drove my boxy, calamine blue Volvo across the street and up the steep driveway to collect Emily. We headed over to Wilson Lane and down MacArthur Boulevard to Georgetown, stopping on the way for lunch at Listrani's restaurant. The dining room was chilly that day, the service was slow, the lettuce desiccated, or maybe everything just seemed lackluster because I was champing at the bit to be at Daysey's side.

While we ate, Emily explained that Daysey's daily rhythm was flipped upside down—she slept all day and read all night—so her friends just let themselves into her house with a door key that was hidden in the flower pot on her front stoop. Daysey, of course, was the champion of the deep sleep, and it was impossible to wake her up simply by ringing her doorbell or knocking on her door. We would let ourselves in, wake her up, and then begin to 'talk' to her through her yellow legal pad.

Promptly at 2 P.M., we arrived at Daysey's door. She lived on a lovely, shady street, not far from Mount Vernon College, where she had taught, and just a few blocks from Georgetown University. Hers was a row house, in a line of attached, two-story homes, each painted a subdued pastel color. An alley stretched along the back of the houses, and a thick stand of tall trees lining the alley gave the neighborhood the feel of a quiet village.

My long trek of fourteen years— although, admittedly, only eight geographic miles—was now at its end. I took a deep breath. Like a fervid pilgrim I had, at last, arrived at the source. I was about to meet the amazing Daysey, hear her recount the story of her life, the story of its suspension, and the story of her resurrection.

My starter questions were racing around in my head. The stacked-high books were slip-sliding in my arms.

Emily, who was by this time elderly, was taking her time digging the key out of the soil in the big flower pot on the front porch, so I bent down and peered into the mail slot. I could see Daysey's dark, wooden, floor-to-ceiling bookcases crammed with books. Hers was the archetypal scholar's home—highly polished oak floors, shelves of leather-bound books, wall-to-wall oriental rugs. Stale pipe smoke wafted out through the mail slot. I could even see Daysey, sound asleep on her tall bed, snoring away.

I realized that I actually knew almost nothing about Daysey. During those many years of thinking about her and researching brain pathologies, I had been mired in the theoretical. I didn't know, for example, where she was born. I knew she had a father and a sister, but why had Emily never said anything about Daysey's mother? Did she have other siblings besides Marion? Did other relatives and friends play significant roles in her unusual life? I didn't know where Daysey had gone to college. I had no idea about her interests besides Freud and Latin. I didn't know the simplest, most basic facts about her life. All I really knew were those few scraps of information and intriguing anecdotes that Emily had told me so many years earlier.

This was the day my ignorance would end.

## Daysey Tells Her Story
## Oxford, 1925

I was thrilled to have the opportunity to study in England, Daysey began. Not only was my life in Oxford infused with gaiety, but the world was rejoicing too. The Great War had ended, and all of Europe was rebuilding.

I was living in Oxford thanks to a one-year fellowship from the Wellesley College alumnae association. I had just completed a masters thesis at Wellesley in philosophy and was continuing my studies of neo-realism in Oxford's B. Litt degree program.

I was an easygoing, happy, and confident graduate student those first two terms, living in rooms on Bradmore Road in the home of a lovely woman named Mrs. Randle. I had both British and American friends at the university. Some had cars, and we would take joy rides, donning our dusters, cranking the engines, inflating the inner tubes of our punctured tires by the side of the road. We loved dancing the Charleston. We drank champagne at formal balls and on New Year's eve. We young women knew little about cocktails but, thanks to Prohibition, we had fun sampling bathtub gin. My life was literally perfect at that time — England was exotic for me, the university was marvelous, my friends were wonderful and fun loving, and our daily afternoon teas were magnificent.

But no excitement in my life ever equalled that of my Christmas vacation in Paris at the end of my first Oxford term.

I had been invited to Aux Chamonix in the French Alps to join American friends for the first part of the holiday. Besides myself, the group that was meeting at the Majestic Hotel was to include two girls, who had been my childhood friends, their mother, who would be our chaperone, and their brother, who was just sixteen and on vacation from his boarding school in Switzerland. In addition, two friends of the sisters, who were students at Vassar College, would join us for the holiday.

One of my new Oxford friends — Henry — asked me at the last minute if he might join me for the vacation. Earlier in the term, Henry had fallen in love with an American student. But, just when things had reached a serious stage between them, Henry's girl told him that she was engaged to someone else back home. He was devastated to be rejected this way and had sought solace confiding in me. For a time, he considered going back to America at Christmas, confronting his rival, and then letting his girl decide between them. Later, he thought better of that plan, which he decided was impetuous. He found himself at loose ends, and that was when he asked to join our party.

I wasn't sure that Henry would like being a lone man among a bevy of young women. But he really did wish to join us, and my friends were glad to include him. They immediately sent him an invitation, and Henry arrived at the Majestic Hotel one day after I did, several days before Christmas.

What a majestic hotel that was, with its elegant lounges and courtly ballrooms, lavish drapes, grand corridors, imposing staircases, and sweeping view of Mont Blanc. We spent our days strolling around the hotel and its grounds, walking into town, eating divine food, and just being happy to be together.

But then Alice, the youngest of the four girls in our group, began to pursue Henry quite openly, even though she was actually engaged to be married to a young man back in the States. Henry grew increasingly uncomfortable with her pursuit, which came to a head when Alice asked him to escort her to the important hotel dance scheduled for Christmas night. He was upset about her aggressiveness and told her that he had joined the group because I was in the party, and of course he had asked me to be his partner for that special night.

Every day, Henry grew more alarmed by the situation that was developing. On December 26, he came to me and said, "Let's go to Paris for New Year's Eve. It's the best night of the year to be in Paris. We can dance in the New Year."

I had planned to stay only a few days at the Majestic in any case, and so I agreed. We travelled back to Paris together the next day. On the train, Henry surprised me.

"You love to travel, and so do I," he said. "Let's get married at the end of term and go to Japan. It should be such an interesting place to see. What do you think?"

I liked Henry. He was attractive and intelligent, but I was far from being in love with him. He was five years younger than I was, which I considered to be another barrier. Besides, I was ambitious for a career, and at that time careers and marriage were not considered a good mix. I had been glad to console Henry and advise him in his unfortunate love affair. And I had been happy to shelter him from Alice's advances. But I was sure Henry was just rebounding from his disappointment and confused and probably exaggerating and misreading his feelings toward me. I told him how I felt, and the marriage discussion ended amicably.

In Paris, we plunged into the most gala holiday I could imagine. Henry knew French culture, because he had spent many summers traveling with his parents in France and throughout Europe. What a thrill for me to go about the city with someone whose ease with French enabled him to converse with taxi drivers and waiters as though he were a native.

The ten days that followed were a joyous revel. I did my Paris sightseeing in the afternoons. Each night, Henry would come from his hotel to pick me up at the Reid House, a residential club for American and French women students right in the center of Paris. We would sally forth to one night club after the other. Henry and I dined and danced in the most luxurious spots, seeing Paris's liveliest haunts. In those days, most young American men in Paris took their girls for an inexpensive evening to a bohemian café—Le Dome or La Rotonde—on the Left Bank. But that was not for us. Nothing

21

was too exclusive for Henry. He was such a sophisticate. And I felt so fortunate.

That was surely my most exciting time of pleasure seeking, and, sadly, the last one before Penzance and a 'cold' brought to an end my enjoyment of life.

I was 32 years old when I got sick, Daysey went on. It was such a shock for me to be ill, because I had never before had a serious sick day in my life. In fact, my application to Oxford contained a brief testimonial from my American doctor about my good health.

*Feb 12, 1925*
*At the request of Miss Marjorie Day, am writing you to state that her health is in excellent condition and she is equal to any Academic Requirement.*

*Yours truly,*
*George C. Anthony*

I had led a completely charmed life until that spring. I had been a truly happy child. College and graduate school, both at Wellesley College, had fully engaged and delighted me. I loved my post-graduate teaching jobs at several preparatory schools. And, when my thesis advisor at Wellesley encouraged me to go on with my studies at Oxford, both she and the president of the college graciously worked with me, advising me how to route my application through the American Association of University Women and direct it to Oxford's Society of Home Students (now called St. Anne's College). The principal of the Home Students, Miss Burrows, then guided me the rest of the way on enrollment and housing procedures.

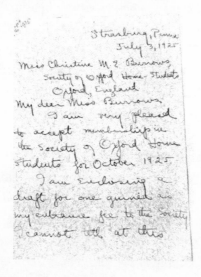

**Daysey's first letter to Miss Christine Burrows, Principal, Oxford Society of Home Students.**

*July 3, 1925*
*My dear Miss Burrows,*
    *I am very pleased to accept membership in the*

*Society of Oxford Home Students for October 1925. I am enclosing a draft for one guinea as my entrance fee to the Society.*

*I cannot tell at this time what my banker's address or my living address will be after leaving America for England about the middle of September, but letters to my home address as given in this letter will reach me until that time.*

*I am looking forward with interest to receiving the information about requirements for a B. Litt degree, which you said would be sent me this summer. The subject which I wish to work in is Philosophy, and I hope to work especially under the realists at Oxford. If there is any advice you can give me about the proper procedure for me to follow now in arranging before the term opens about my course of study I should very much appreciate it. Also, if there is any circular of information in regard to addresses to which I may write in arranging for residence in Oxford for the coming year, I should be glad to have it.*

*I shall plan to be in Oxford at least a week before the opening of the Michaelmas Term and shall come immediately to you for further advice and information.*

*Many thanks for your kind letter.*

*Sincerely yours,*
*Marjorie C. Day*

**Daysey's second letter to Miss Burrows.**

*August 31, 1925*
*Dear Miss Burrows,*

*Many thanks to you for your letter of July 21st enclosing advice about my plan of work and search for a room in Oxford.*

*As to the former, I hope I can supply enough data so that you can make application for my entrance as a probationer student for the Bachelor of Letters degree. I realize that the time is so short before I shall be leaving this country that very likely you will not be able to reply to me again, but I trust that you will be able, from my suggesting in general the line of work I wish to take up, to make the preliminary arrangements about my being entered for work under a preliminary supervisor.*

*I think if I could submit my manuscript copy accepted for publication in the German philosophical magazine (Archiv fur Philosophie) that would make more definite the trend of my proposed work in Philosophy. I shall bring that copy with me, for I do not like to entrust it to mailing at this late date, and it did not occur to me to present it earlier. Miss Calkins of Wellesley College suggested that I submit it. That paper is on "Neo-Realism as a Doctrine of Mind," and neo-realism is the field of philosophy in which I wish especially to work. Within that field the philosophical problems that I want to make my special topics of study are the nature of mind and the mind-body relation. Can you from this meager data proceed with my application?*

*I am sailing from this country September 23d, and shall come immediately to Oxford after landing in Plymouth about the third or fourth of October. I shall come immediately to you, if I may, to find out just what applications, etc. are necessary for me to make before the opening of term.*

*I have written to Oxenford Hall to find out if it would be possible for me to have a room there while I look up some of the possibilities of rooms with a private hostess. I am very grateful for the names and addresses of hostesses given me in your last letter, and I hope to make final arrangements with one of them for a room for the year.*

  *Thanking you for your letter and advice I am,*
    *Very truly yours,*
    *Marjorie C. Day*

When I arrived in Oxford in 1925, I found that I had been assigned to work with two of the university's luminaries, the senior philosophy tutor, Horace William Brindley Joseph of New College, who was one of Oxford's realists, and the classics tutor, Annie Mary Anne Henley Rogers, who was Oxford's first woman don. Like all home students, I had to enroll as a "probationer" that first term, but, by the time I returned from my Paris vacation, I had been promoted to full student status. Unlike the earlier Home Students, who were required to attend classes in the men's colleges accompanied by older women, their 'knitting chaperones,' the Home Students of my era were allowed to go to our classes by ourselves.

The fall and winter terms — Michaelmas and Hilary — were so stimulating and challenging, and all went well for me in every way. When Hilary term ended, several friends and I packed up our books and clothing and headed to Penzance for a study holiday. We had chosen Penzance, an ancient marketing town and port (it has bronze-age and iron-age relics), because of its beautiful, clean beaches. The weather there is known to be milder than weather anywhere else in England, thanks to the breezes that flow into the town from the Gulf Stream and the surrounding seas. We were more than ready for that warmth and for a lengthy period of relaxation.

But shortly after we arrived in Penzance, I was struck by the most peculiar cold I had ever experienced. It had a most harrowing symptom: sleeplessness — not just the inability to get a normal night's sleep, but absolute wakefulness night after night.

Ten nights of misery had turned me into a walking ghost. Food was disgusting, exercise impossible, and I was exhausted. My friends were enjoying strawberries and thick Devonshire cream, but I found even those delicacies repellent.

In Penzance, my eyesight began to fail. I had planned plenty of study and writing for the break, which all Oxford students were obliged to do in the long, six-week 'vacs.' How frightening it was to sit before the fire, book in hand, and find that I couldn't understand what I was reading, and worse, that the print was becoming illegible.

My friends began urging me to go back up to London to see a doctor. At first I refused, but finally my resistance gave way, and, weary and exhausted, I set out for the long train ride back to town.

I knew as I headed north that something was seriously amiss. The countryside appeared completely menacing: endless rows of cabbages were grinning at me; no, they seemed to be mocking me. This was not the charming Devonshire landscape that I had admired on my train ride down.

One of my American friends, Julia, was living in London at that time, and she met me at the train station and took me directly to her Harley Street physician. He began a relentless but unsuccessful physiological investigation, but he could not identify a specific organic cause for my utter exhaustion and insomnia. Then he embarked on a psychiatric probe, questioning me and then Julia, asking whether I had emotional problems, home or family problems, had been happy at Oxford, had been in love, etc. Both of us were able to honestly answer that I had been very happy at Oxford, had made many friends, and had socialized a great deal with both English and American students. I had had no love affairs, but I did have close friends.

The doctor prescribed sedation and rest and then admitted me to the American Hospital in St. John's Wood.

My immediate need was for sleep, but sleep was elusive. The doctor was puzzled, saying he feared I was in for a long and serious illness, but he could not put his diagnostic finger on the cause. I mentioned that, during Michaelmas term, I had gone to see a doctor in Oxford, because I had felt a strange achiness in my joints. But that problem, which the Oxford doctor suspected might be arthritis, did not seem to be connected with my new complaints.

I was supposed to take a short walk every day, see the doctor, and rest. But I could barely make my way down the hall to the bathing facilities, just twenty steps from my room. When I did get to the bath each day, I would lie there for an hour at a time and wonder how I would be able to pull myself together sufficiently to crawl back out of the warm water and return to my room. I lay there, yearning to soak forever in the soothing liquid.

Sleep was a losing battle. The nurse would stand at the foot of my bed and plead with me, "Miss Day, you must sleep."

"Don't you suppose I want to sleep?" I'd said. "Why don't you give me something to make me sleep?"

"We are already giving you the strongest, safe dosage the doctor can prescribe," she had said in reply.

Nothing countered my unyielding wakefulness.

One awful evening, the hall maid, Fanny, who brought my meals to my room, stood in the doorway with the tray. Then, to my surprise, she suddenly shrank until she was just the size of a doll. I was clear headed enough to know that this was some sort of illusion, but I couldn't imagine what freakish thing was happening to my eyes, or why.

Another evening, after supper, I was sitting by the bedroom fireplace with my slippered feet extended comfortably toward the blaze. I looked down at my bare right ankle and was surprised to discover a blister as big as a quarter on my leg. My foot had been too close to the fire. But I had felt no sensation! I thought then, "My entire sensory apparatus must be going out of gear."

The hospital stay proved of no help. After ten days, I was still not rested, and yet it was time for me to return to Oxford for the opening of term. The doctor in London advised me to forget about school and go up to the Shetland lake region for a complete rest. But I resisted.

And so, though I felt like a walking wraith, I let Julia lead me to the Oxford-London train. The car was filled with laughing, chattering students. The noise and the clamor were almost unbearable; I remember wanting to plunge out of the train window to get away from it all. But, of course, I restrained myself and somehow managed to endure the battering noise.

When I arrived  on  the  doorstep of  my

Oxford home, my kind landlady, Mrs. Randle, gave me a worried, solicitous look.

"Miss Day, are you ill?" she asked.

"I've had a bit of a cold," I said.

The next day was dreadful. I was still trying to resume my normal life. Mrs. Randle said she would send a breakfast tray up to the drawing room so that I could eat quietly by the open fire. This was the day I was to begin Trinity term. I needed to put on my academic gown, ride over to the lecture room, and be in my seat by 10 A.M.

I stood in the drawing room window, trying to summon the energy that I needed. By coincidence, the don who was advising me on my research rode by on his bicycle, robes flapping. How odd: he was pedaling his bicycle, but the bicycle appeared to remain stationary, and he seemed not to be covering any ground at all. "My confounded eyes," I thought.

I decided that I should go to see Miss Burrows, my principal, instead of going directly to the lecture hall. I felt I should explain to her what was going on with me and what I knew of my situation--my strange cold, my inability to sleep, and now these bizarre optical illusions.

The short ride to Miss Burrows's residence was terrifying. I noticed that the faces

of all of the students I passed were splotched with some disgusting lesions. I remember thinking, "How peculiar. I've spent all of my life in academia, I've always been at home with students, but now everyone seems completely repulsive to me."

Miss Burrows gave me a troubled look, much as Mrs. Randle had, and said, "You're ill. I think we should arrange for you to go back to America."

"But, my fellowship," I said. "I can't leave."

"When you are well, you can come back," Miss Burrows said. "You can always come back. But now I'm going to get in touch with someone to arrange passage at once to take you home."

I went outside and got on my bicycle to ride back to my rooms. But I didn't get there. I lost control of my bicycle, ran into a guard, and then collapsed.

I was not clear headed again—not myself—for seventeen years.

**Cablegram to Dr. George Ezra Day, Strasburg, PA, U.S.A. from Miss Burrows.**

*April 28, 1926.*
*Daughter seriously ill. Come at once.*
*Signed: Miss Christine M.E. Burrows*

**Letter from Daysey's hostess Mrs. Randle, to Miss Burrows, the principal of the Oxford Society of Home Students.**

*May 3, 1926*
*Dear Miss Burrows,*

*I am so grieved that there is not better news of Miss Day. We are all so fond of her, my children just love her. She was always so sweet and patient. One feels so very very sorry for her parents — how dreadfully anxious they must be.*

*I trust there will be better news soon.*

*Yours sincerely,*
*Joan Randle*

## Sources

Let me interrupt the narrative here, while Daysey is tragically out cold, to describe the provenance of those letters from the 1920s. Daysey had the devastating cablegram that Miss Burrows had sent to her parents. But the letters that Daysey wrote to Miss Burrows the summer before she went to Oxford, the testimonial from Daysey's American doctor to the university, and the letter from Mrs. Randle to Miss Burrows were all part of Daysey's Oxford University file, which an archivist at Oxford located and sent to me long after Daysey died.

Let me pause further for a confession: I never actually met Daysey. I never had a chance to directly question her or hear her talk about her extraordinary life. How, then, can I know her actual words and present to you her first-hand account of her experiences? Let me back up and explain.

That day in 1991, when my neighbor, Emily, and I were standing at Daysey's front door, I had ample time to peer through the mail slot to contemplate those shiny floors, Daysey's books and bookshelves, and her stale tobacco fumes, because Emily was not immediately finding the front door key. At first, Emily casually brushed aside the top layer of soil in the flower pot. But then I noticed that she had begun to dig frantically in the soil, like a desperate dog trying to unearth a deeply buried bone.

"I can't find the key," Emily had said, with a very worried look on her face. "Perhaps the back door is open." She stepped down from the porch, hurried to the end of the block, and disappeared along the side of the row houses. Soon, I heard her banging on Daysey's back door. I put my books down on the stoop, walked over to the flower pot, and stuck my fingers into the soil, but I couldn't unearth the key either.

Emily came back to the front, dug deeper in the flower pot, pounded once more on the front door, raced around to the back again, and whacked repeatedly on the door back there.

Finally, it was clear: we were not going to rouse Daysey. If anyone knew how to sleep deeply, surely Daysey was the one.

Emily had gotten into a sweat; I was in a complete funk. All of my excitement, anticipation, and preparations were rapidly

going down the tubes. Eventually, we had no further options. I deposited my offering of books at Daysey's front door, walked back off the porch, got into the car, and drove us home.

The next day, Emily called me. Daysey's cleaning lady had been careless: she had left the house key inside the house when she had finished her work the previous day at noon. Now, twenty-four hours later, the key was back out in the flower pot, and Emily said that we could reschedule our visit for another time.

But a return visit did not come to pass.

Daysey had a stroke two weeks later, and on September 24, 1991, she died at a nursing center. She was 98 years old.

Several months after Daysey's death, I went with Emily to a memorial service that Mount Vernon College held to honor its beloved professor. I listened as Daysey's colleagues spoke of her brilliance and her unique life. I simply could not believe that I had squandered so many years foolishly speculating about Daysey rather than actually talking to her.

Time passed and I never stopped wondering about Daysey's illness experience and her resurrection. When, in 1993, Richard Selzer published his book *Raising the Dead*, I wondered whether his brush with mortality during his twenty-three-day deep sleep brought on by Legionnaire's disease had any relevance to Daysey's experience. Selzer's "meditation on coma" was written from his perspectives as both surgeon and patient. He said that his walk "in the valley of the shadow of death" had been like "being encased in a layer of wax … nothing to do but wait and listen to the silences rubbing against each other …"

I was drawn in by Selzer's lyrical images of the protagonist, lying still on the gurney, patiently awaiting revitalization.

"… Beneath the closed eyelids his eyeballs roll slowly from side to side, then dart the way fish will move in a pond … Then he hears a wingbeat and feels something fugitive, immaterial, a beige veil being drawn from his face, slowly at first then faster, until the final whisk is like a slap … the first breath … a deep sigh … either of sorrow or of satisfaction …"

Was this what Daysey had felt during her illness and during her awakening? Had she, too, felt that same first breath? Had she also released that same deep sigh?

Abruptly Selzer backed down completely from his coma narrative, shattering my musings. "The Truth?" he wrote, "I don't remember a darn thing."

Seventeen more years went by. I remained always on the lookout for revivification stories and regularly ran new literature searches on brain diseases. But the trail to Daysey had turned icy cold.

Finally, in 2008, my luck changed. I was working on an essay about ethical dilemmas raised when people are in comas and persistent vegetative states. Sometimes family members are forced to ponder whether and when to pull the plug on their loved one. Sometimes disagreements arise between members of the patient's family or between family members and the doctors or the hospital administrators. Such contentious bedside quandaries have grown more common as state-of-the-art medical technologies — typically, the respirator — save people from dying but do not really keep them living substantive lives. Increasingly, these clashes end up being resolved through highly visible, costly, and nasty cases in the courts.

I had decided to try to include in the essay something about Daysey's experience. I was not sure exactly how her illness might be relevant to what I was writing, but I was eager to see if I could fold something about her story into my commentary.

I pulled out my "Daysey" file, which had grown thick over the years. I had copious notes and hundreds of articles on brain development, sleeping sickness, various forms of encephalitis, comas, brain death, and related topics, and a list of the books and memoirs that I'd read or intended to read.

Daysey's name still did not pop up in a google search, but I found two articles about her — a tribute published in the Washington Post several months after she died and a longer, four-page article in Washingtonian Magazine, which had been published the summer after her death.

The Washingtonian article was based on a group interview that the author had conducted with Daysey's colleagues and friends some time after that memorial service at Mount Vernon College. I was fascinated to see that each of Daysey's friends, including my neighbor, Emily (EL), told the story somewhat differently. Each of the interviewees had been close to Daysey, but they couldn't come to consensus on anything— what she said had happened to her, where she was when she got sick, what year it was, what year she woke back up.

*PB: I think she was bitten by a tsetse fly. This may have happened in Africa while she was waiting for a boat.*

*EL: Oh, no, no, no, no. Daysey was never in Africa. And she wasn't waiting for any boat.*

*PB: She woke up after seventeen years and went to the Library of Congress and read the newspapers from when she'd been asleep.*

*EL: Daysey had gone to the New York Public Library, not the Washington library, and she had read just the first page stories of the Times from the past seventeen years.*

They kept on arguing. Clearly, Rashomon was having a field day among Daysey's friends.

And then came the astounding statement made by Flora Harper to the article's author:

*FH: Daysey wrote up her own story. It wasn't published, but I will send it to you. You should really read it to get the details down.*

What? Daysey had written a memoir?

I looked up Flora Harper in the D.C. white pages. A Flora Harper was, in fact, listed, living not far from Mount Vernon College. This had to be the same Flora Harper. I wrote her a letter describing my friendship with Emily (who had since died) and my longstanding interest in Daysey.

A week later, "Mimi" Flora Harper called me. She had received my letter, and she would be happy to give me Daysey's memoir. But she was in Massachusetts at the moment and was about to fly from there to Europe for a couple of weeks. She promised she would give me a call as soon as she got back to Washington. She had been a close friend of Daysey for forty years, had been the dean of Mount Vernon College in the years when Daysey taught there, and had, in fact, hired Daysey to teach at the college. Mimi was actually at the cottage in Massachusetts that Daysey had bequeathed to her when Daysey died.

Those weeks waiting for Mimi to return were agonizing. But finally she got back in town and called immediately to invite me to join her for dinner at the Cosmos Club.

I spent the afternoon floating, distracted. I was about to meet an actual friend of Daysey so many years after Daysey had died! What would I learn? And what would I discover in the memoir? Would any or many of my imaginings from all those years be confirmed?

I drove down Massachusetts Avenue to the Cosmos Club on that starry night, pulled up at the back door of the club, gave my keys to the valet, and headed inside. Mimi had told me to meet her in the lobby, and as I rounded the corner and entered that imposing room — marble floors, large oriental rugs, fire places, stuffed chairs and couches, ferns and orchids — there stood a tall, slim woman, who clearly was Mimi. She was wearing a pastel sweater, a silky scarf, a slim tweed skirt, and was holding a small purse in her hand. We shook hands and introduced ourselves. The second words out of Mimi's mouth were, "I couldn't find the memoir. My house is a mess of papers at the moment. I need more time to look for it, but I know it's there somewhere. I just have to search a bit more."

To say that I was dispirited is putting things mildly. "Devastated" works nicely. Foiled again. Still, I forced a smile to my face and followed Mimi into the dim dining room. The maitre d' showed us to a table for two next to the wine cellar and across from a glass case filled with Old Spode dishes. Mimi started in right away, telling me about her friendship with Daysey, and her cheerful, upbeat voice helped me recover from this huge setback, the latest of so many, which, in any case, I could do absolutely nothing about.

Mimi had many stories that night and in the coming months. She and Daysey had become friends as soon as Daysey moved to Washington, and their friendship ended only when Daysey died. She had "absolutely loved" Daysey. I worried that asking Mimi to talk about Daysey might be painful, but Mimi said, to the contrary, it was just wonderful to think about her again.

When I left the Cosmos Club that night, my brain was a jumble of new images, renewed excitement, worry, and deep disappointment. I had just learned so many new things about Daysey from Mimi, and I felt that I was getting closer and closer to Daysey's own story as well. But, would it elude me again?

Another week passed. Then Mimi called

to say that she had located the memoir, and I could come to her house to pick it up. I drove along the same route that I had taken with Emily seventeen years earlier—but this time, above the speed limit—down MacArthur Boulevard, past Listrani's restaurant where Emily and I had stopped for lunch, and then turned down toward the Potomac River to the short street where Mimi lives. I parked in front of her house and walked up the sloping path to her door. I rang the bell and, while I waited for her to come, looked into her glassed-in porch, which was filled with spectacular orchids.

Mimi had several new stories for me that day. She and her husband, Bob, had played "a peculiar game of three-handed bridge" with Daysey every Friday night for the last twenty years of Daysey's life. Sometimes Bob would drive Daysey up to Massachusetts to her summer cottage, and those trips always generated funny tales of adventures. Daysey was so brilliant yet so frustrated by simple things, like cars and appliances. Mimi laughed recalling a time when she had stopped by Daysey's apartment and found her blowing dust crazily around the room; Daysey had somehow reversed the flow on her vacuum cleaner.

I asked Mimi about Daysey's family,

because, at the Cosmos Club, she had briefly mentioned Daysey's sister, Marion, and Daysey's mother, Ella. Yes, she had spent time with both of them over the years, and she had even gone with Daysey back to her hometown when first her mother and then her sister had died. All four of the Days, she said, were buried in that town, Strasburg, Pennsylvania, in the graveyard behind the Presbyterian Church.

When our conversation wound down, Mimi handed me a bright yellow folder. I didn't even glance inside it until I got back down to my car and had buckled my seat belt. Then, I couldn't wait another second. Inside the folder were seventy-eight typed, double-spaced pages, titled *Life Suspended*, written by Daysey herself sometime in the 1970s.

I took a small detour into Georgetown to its famous cupcake store and bought myself a rich, chocolate-hazelnut cupcake; when I got nearer home, I stopped for a grande cappuccino. Back at home I settled in at the dining room table, feasting for a full three hours on cupcake, cappuccino, and Daysey's story as told by Daysey herself.

## Pursuing the Story

Daysey was a lively story teller, but she had written a cryptic memoir. For some reason, she had anonymized many essential details, not giving her hometown a name, or naming her parents, or her college. She also did not name the hospitals where she spent so many years, the preparatory schools where she taught before and after her illness, the towns where she lived all through her life, and many of the people in her story. But, luckily, I had Mimi, and she was able to give me key place names—Wellesley College; Strasburg, Pennsylvania—as well as the names of some of the people Daysey referred to, and so my research was jump started.

I contacted the archivist at Wellesley College, who sent me Daysey's transcript, course lists, alumnae notes, masters thesis, and other documents. Daysey's frequent letters to the Wellesley alumnae magazine nicely mapped out all of the steps in her professional life and many of her other activities, as well as the addresses of her homes, beginning with her birthplace and ending with her final home in Georgetown. Only her residences during her illness and recovery were missing.

I contacted the archivist at Mount Vernon College, who found the syllabuses for all of the courses that Daysey taught. Each syllabus was hand written in Daysey's signature Palmer Method script. That archivist also found photographs of Daysey in numerous yearbooks and a number of other useful resources.

I searched the web, looking for medical archivists in England and Pennsylvania who might be able to tell me which hospitals treated Daysey during her illness. After months of intensive sleuth work by the Oxfordshire medical archivist and six formal emails between us—"Dear Mrs. Boardman"; "Dear Professor Guyer"—I knew that something had changed when Elizabeth Boardman began the seventh email to me this way: "Dear Ruth (if I may)." Then she continued:

*You will be delighted to hear that the copy of the letter you sent gave us the clue we needed, and we have found Marjorie Cornelia Day's medical record.*

Elizabeth also figured out where in Oxford Daysey had been enrolled, and she connected me to the archivist at St. Anne's College, who sent me the letters and other records in Daysey's university file.

No state medical archivist would tell me anything about Daysey's many years in the Pennsylvania hospitals. Their reasons for refusing my requests included HIPPA violations, burnt archives, and records sealed for one hundred years. But a key doctor in Philadelphia, who had known Daysey when they both were children and had treated her during her long illness, recorded an oral history late in his life, and he talked about the powerful effects that Daysey's recovery had on his clinical thinking.

In 2011, the archives for the Rockport (Massachusetts) Lodge were catalogued and became available, and in them I found letters, photographs, and other records of Daysey's many summers there as the head of the Lodge's recreation program.

Daysey expressed both in her memoir and in her notes to her Wellesley classmates that she hoped that her recollections of her journey through coma, insanity, and recovery would be published. But that never happened. One publisher told her that the 1946 novel, *The Snake*

*Pit*, had pre-empted her chances for publication. That novel, named for the long-discarded practice of tossing the insane into snake pits in hopes that the shock of the experience would jolt them back to sanity, resonated with Daysey when she read that story some years after her recovery.

"That is exactly how it was," Daysey wrote. The novel's protagonist describes dehumanizing conditions in a huge psychiatric institution, and her experiences mirrored Daysey's own exactly. Daysey felt that she could have corroborated every word, from the brutal physical conditions present in the hospital to the profound isolation and total loss of engagement with the outside world that she experienced. The main difference was that, for Daysey, the story was true and the ignominy lasted much longer than it did for the heroine of the novel.

*The Snake Pit* later was made into a movie, and both the book and the film raised public awareness to the inhumane conditions that prevailed in psychiatric hospitals in the United States at the time. But real reforms were only implemented after a second book, *The Shame of the States*, was published in 1948. The author of that book, Albert Deutsch, a reporter and historian, had sneaked into a number of large state hospitals and had taken photographs of nude, huddled patients, thereby documenting the indignities for all to see. Deutsch's book put sequestered psychiatric patients back on the radar screens of the public.

Something my neighbor, Emily, told me had led me to believe that Daysey was from the midwest. But now it turned out that Daysey was a Pennsylvanian, as was I, and her hometown was just fifty minutes from my hometown, where my mother still lived. At Thanksgiving, in 2008, my mother, my older daughter, my husband, and I drove over to have a look at Strasburg, Pennsylvania. The Wellesley transcript gave Daysey's address there as 7 Decatur Street.

The Days' stately home was two blocks from the center of town, a brick colonial, revival-style structure with four columns on the front porch, three dormers above the porch, and a fanlight over the door. It had been built in the late 1890s and exuded comfort, stability, and prosperity.

The town looked to us much as it must have appeared to Daysey and her family. Strasburg was already "historic" when the Days were living there, and in fact, it celebrated its centenary when Daysey was just a child.

We drove around Strasburg and easily found the Presbyterian church. It was a chilly grey day and my mother was not in good health. So, when we pulled up to the church's cemetery gate, my daughter, my husband, and I hopped out of the car and left my mother sitting in the warm car with the motor on.

We fanned out across the cemetery, each walking, head down, through a different section, in search of the Days' headstones. We were not sure exactly what the Days' plot might look like. Then, my cell phone beeped and a text message popped up on the screen from my daughter: "Over here."

The headstones for Daysey, Marion, and their parents were together, side by side, in front

of a large, simple stone—Day. The discovery was, for me, both incredibly thrilling and tremendously sad. Ella (Daysey's mother) had died at age 88, Marion (her sister) at 72, George (her father) at 68. Daysey, the one whose life had been so fraught, died at 98, having outlived them all.

## 1893
## The Back Story

Daysey was born on July 7, 1893 in the charming rural Pennsylvania town of Strasburg. As she wrote in her memoir, her life, too, was charmed until everything went haywire in her thirty-second year.

Daysey's father—George Ezra Day—was the revered town doctor and her mother—Ella Rakestraw Day—was a much-loved 'local girl.' Her maternal grandmother lived just around the corner from the family, as did two of her aunts.

Daysey and her little sister, Marion, were always on the go. They played "school" for endless hours with their friends--Marion and the others always the willing pupils and Daysey always the wise, omniscient teacher. Both girls were able athletes, riding and jumping their father's horses and playing baseball and tennis. Daysey was the intellectual; Marion, the artist.

George's clinic was on the first floor of the family home. Patients would stop by throughout the day and sit in the waiting room chatting with one another until George could see them. Dr. Day was known for dispensing "little pink pills, whether or not we needed them," one old-timer told me when I visited Strasburg. The woman was in her early nineties when we spoke, but she clearly remembered Dr. Day, whom she described as "short, stout, and kindly," always sporting a Van Dyke beard. Not only had Dr. Day officiated at the woman's birth but the birth announcements that her family had sent out had been designed by Marion, who at the time was just a teen.

A second ninety-year-old woman from Strasburg told me that Daysey was a legend in the community long before she got sick—a smart, gregarious, and spirited little girl. "Everyone loved Daysey," she told me. And everyone was heartbroken when the tragedy struck. Thus it was that, more than seventy-five years after the last of the Days had moved away from Strasburg, these two women and others in the town clearly remembered not just the family but also their traumatic story.

Daysey and Marion attended the local schools, but, when Daysey graduated from Strasburg High School in 1908, her parents decided to send her for an additional year to the

Shippen School, which was a new type of finishing school in nearby Lancaster. The school prepared bright pupils for entry into top colleges, including some of the new, elite women's colleges. Shippen's curriculum was classical and rigorous, and the school brooked no nonsense about attendance. "As the day's session closes at half after three," notes the Shippen brochure, "it is asked that all appointments on school days with dentists, music teachers, or dressmakers be made after that hour."

One of Daysey's favorite teachers at Shippen was Grace Phemister, who had recently graduated from Wellesley College and was teaching French and English. She encouraged Daysey to go to Wellesley, which Daysey was able to do without even filling out an application; the Shippen certificate was all she needed to get in.

Daysey was seventeen when she arrived at Wellesley in 1910. She quickly made her mark among her classmates, elected immediately as a "factotum" to the student government. Also that year, she was chosen to represent her class at the springtime Tree Day celebration as the "Receiver of Spade," an honorific conferred on the wittiest girl in the class.

The fanfare at Tree Day included tableaux, songs, and speeches. After a sophomore gave a pompous speech, she handed the heavy metal spade to Daysey, who then launched into her own outrageous speech. Next, the gardeners lowered the sapling into the ground, and Daysey and her classmates dumped spades of soil into the hole. More than sixty years later, one of Daysey's classmates reported that their class's purple beech was still sturdy and huge, right next to the college library.

Daysey took a heavy course load during her four years at Wellesley, double majoring in Latin and English literature. She studied the prose works of Pliny, Livy, Tacitus, and Cicero, the poetry of Horace and others of the Augustan Age, the comedies of Plautus and Terence, and the satires of Juvenal and Horace. She also spent a year doing Latin composition. Her deep immersion in Latin accounts for how, when her long illness finally came to its end, she simply "took up" Latin again, just as any educated citizen of ancient Rome would have done.

Daysey's other big interest was psychology-philosophy, a 'hot' field at Wellesley at the time. The chair of the joint psychology-philosophy department, Mary Whiton Calkins, was one of the first American professors whose students actually conducted experiments on vision, hearing, and other measurable phenomena. Other colleges at the time were still teaching the more abstract "mental philosophy." Miss Calkins was the professor who later encouraged Daysey to go to Oxford. And Helen Temple Cooke, also in the psychology-philosophy department, was the professor who started Daysey on her pre-illness teaching career and later got her back into teaching after their serendipitous encounter when Daysey was, once again, among the living.

Daysey's transcript also listed semester-long or year-long courses in Biblical history, the political histories of England and the French revolution, economics, chemistry, mathematics, zoology, English literature, English composition, and Greek. Yet, Daysey was not a grind. The Wellesley yearbook, Legenda, published in 1914, is filled with pictures and entries of Daysey participating in sports, theater productions, student government activities, and college traditions. She was a clever, funny, creative, adventuresome, and popular member of her class.

In 1914, Daysey graduated from Wellesley with a B.A. degree. Her official yearbook photograph shows a thoughtful young woman, hair parted down the center and tucked up at the back of her head. She, like her classmates, is formally dressed in a starched, high-collared white shirt with a ribbon brooch at her neck.

Daysey characterized her years at Wellesley as idyllic and her association with the college and with her classmates as one of the strongest and consistent anchors of her life.

When she graduated, she accepted a teaching job in Swarthmore, PA, at the Mary Lyons School, which, like Shippen, was a feeder school for elite women's colleges.

Marjorie C. Day
Strasburg,
Pennsylvania

**Note in the Wellesley alumnae magazine, February 23, 1918. Sent from Mary Lyons School, Swarthmore, PA.**

*This is my second year of instilling a love for the classics in the wild hearts of Mary Lyon-esses, in reality of cramming Latin enough into many hard little heads to get said heads into college. I am beginning to feel quite a veteran at the business now that I have former pupils who are sophomores in college. One of my "finished products" of last year is now a freshman at Wellesley, and I have lots of others headed in that same sensible direction. It revives one's youth to live over college with the "next generation."*

In 1919, Daysey moved back to Wellesley, invited there by Miss Cooke, who was both a professor at Wellesley and the head mistress of the Tenacre School at Dana Hall. Daysey taught Latin at Tenacre and soon was also involved again at the college, taking courses toward her masters degree in the psychology-philosophy department and also working as a teaching assistant.

In 1922, she completed her masters thesis at Wellesley. The thesis addressed the nature of human consciousness and was later published in the German journal *Archiv fur Philosophie*. She continued to teach at Tenacre and continued to take courses at the college, immersing herself in ethics, neo-realism, religious philosophies, introspection, behaviorism, and the psychology of the unconscious. Of course, the form of unconsciousness that interested her in those days—perhaps better labeled "subconscious-ness"—was not the form of unconsciousness into which she would soon be plunged.

**Note in the Wellesley alumnae magazine, 1924.
Sent from Strasburg, PA.**

*Since 1922 (and several years before that date), I've been sticking around Wellesley, teaching in the Psych Department and also at Dana Hall schools, doing some studying too in Psychology and Philosophy all the while with the idea of going on for another degree eventually. I'll be away somewhere next year studying — likely at Oxford. Need you ask of my husband and children?*

## 1926

## Sick

The final entry in Daysey's Oxford University record was this one:

*Returned T[rinity] T[erm] 1926 v[ery] ill -? [en]cephalitis leth[argica]. Father came over & removed her to Warneford Hosp[ital]. Name kept on books & dues paid for T[rinity] T[erm ]1926. Cannot continue B. Litt. at present.*

Those few handwritten words — "v. ill -?

cephalitis leth."—totally surprised me. Daysey never had any idea what hit her—not in her memoir, not in her other writings, and not in conversations with her friends. Yet here was the university's registrar recording a diagnosis for Daysey as soon as she fell ill. Why hadn't Daysey ever connected the dots between her bizarre and lengthy illness with the new, brutal disease— encephalitis lethargica—that was already epidemic in England at the time she fell ill? Why hadn't anyone told her what this registrar knew?

When I saw those scribbled words, I raced back to the library to look more closely at the literature on encephalitis lethargica. In my earlier research, this peculiar form of encephalitis had intrigued me, but it had not seemed to fit Daysey's clinical profile as I knew it. Every report that I had read indicated that the disease was always permanently debilitating or fatal, and Daysey had not died and had, in fact, recovered fully.

The British had nicknamed encephalitis lethargica "sleepy sickness." At onset, encephalitis lethargica triggered dramatic changes in its victims' sleep patterns that were reminiscent of sleep disturbances common in people with African sleeping sickness. But sleepy sickness was completely distinct etiologically from

African sleeping sickness, which, even in the 1920s, was known to be caused by a parasite, *Trypanosoma brucei*.

Clusters of cases of sleepy sickness first showed up in Paris and Vienna in the winters of 1915-1916 and 1916-1917. By the early 1920s, encephalitis lethargica had become epidemic in England, and it had also begun appearing in the United States. The epidemic continued to spread in Europe until 1927, when, mysteriously, it simply vanished. And since that time, only sporadic cases have been reported anywhere in the world.

The sleep disturbances associated with encephalitis lethargica were varied: some patients slept too much, others not at all (those patients had agrypnia, or complete insomnia), and many slept during the day and were awake all night.

For most victims, encephalitis lethargica began with a sore throat or, as Daysey said of the onset of her illness, a "peculiar cold." Most reported double vision, as Daysey had, and many experienced other problems with their eyes—twitching, muscle paralysis, drooping lids.

As the disease progressed and brain cells deteriorated, victims developed wide-ranging psychiatric and behavioral symptoms. Some became "rude and cheeky"; they would shout obscenities, spit in public, be uncharacteristically crude, obsess about sex. Some grew mute and apathetic; others grew agitated, irritable, and anxious. Many reported terrifying hallucinations; others acted out in irrational and uncharacteristic ways. Some developed a particular suite of symptoms collectively termed parkinsonism — tremors, muscle rigidity, a shuffling gait, slowed speech, and a mask-like facial expression. Most survivors, including Daysey, remembered essentially nothing about the period when they were ill.

The fear was that the disease was highly contagious, although it turned out not to be. (The medical journals of the 1920s cited only a few examples in which two people in a single household developed encephalitis lethargica at the same time.)

An Austrian neuroscientist, Constantin von Economo, first characterized the disease in 1916 and coined its evocative name. He had been caring for soldiers with head injuries at the General Hospital in Vienna when he began noticing an epidemic of lethargy in a subset of his patients. Their behavior reminded him of patients he had once read about, a "soporose" group who, eighty-five years earlier, had grown pathologically lethargic while recovering from attacks of scarlet fever.

Von Economo speculated that the sore throat associated with encephalitis lethargica was caused by bacteria in the same taxonomic group that caused scarlet fever. To explain the skewed biological clocks of the patients, von Economo invoked a second agent, probably a virus, that could home specifically to a switch in the brain controlling a previously uncharacterized sleep-wake center and mess it up.

Through autopsies, von Economo catalogued numerous changes in the victims' brains: major alterations in the brain's overall architecture, shrunken or missing nerve cells, and atypical inflammatory cells infiltrating the brain tissue. Although his observations did not lead to beneficial therapies for his patients, they did prove useful for subsequent mapping of discrete brain activities to specific brain areas.

In general, those who did not die from encephalitis lethargica experienced lingering and calamitous psychiatric and movement disorders throughout their lives. (At the time that Daysey got sick, 20-40% of those who contracted encephalitis lethargica in England died almost immediately.) The most common enduring signs and symptoms were expressionless faces and stiff gaits. The rare patient who made a complete recovery was one who endured just a short acute illness, in the range of two to four months. No one ever described a patient who was critically ill for seventeen years and then was fine. That is, no one ever described a patient like Daysey.

Von Economo found no evidence that the encephalitis lethargica epidemic was an after effect of the 1918 influenza epidemic. He had seen patients with encephalitis lethargica for a full three years before any patients developed that flu. Other physicians at the time were trying to make such an association, but recent molecular studies show that von Economo was correct. The thawed-out brains of patients who died in the 1920s from encephalitis lethargic have no tell-tale genetic material from the 1918 influenza virus. Furthermore, that virus, which has now been fully characterized, resides and reproduces in the respiratory system, not in the brain; there is, thus, no way that virus could have triggered the wide-ranging neurologic effects common to and characteristic of the encephalitis lethargica survivors.

Contemporary researchers suspect that streptococcal bacteria triggered an antibody response in the encephalitis lethargica victims that was able, accidentally, to react with the brain's basal ganglia and damage it. That could account for the common, lingering neuropsychiatric symptoms seen in most surviving patients. Similar cross-reactive, auto-immune responses are known in a number of other diseases. Exactly why and how autoimmunity develops in some individuals and not in others remains unclear. And why streptococcal infections of the 1920s produced encephalitis lethargica for only a decade and then stopped doing that is another unanswered question.

To this day, no one has figured out whether a virus, a parasite, a bacterium, a prion (the type of infectious agent that is associated with bizarre brain anomalies, like scrapie and mad cow disease), something in the environment, or several of these caused the devastating encephalitis lethargica epidemic.

## 1926
## Coma

In the first days after Daysey collapsed, she was moved to a boarding house at 7 Mansfield Road in Oxford, where the hostess, Mrs. Ridley, was able to provide rooms for Daysey, for the nurses who had been hired from the nearby Acland Hospital to care for her around the clock, and for her father, when he arrived in England.

The university called in Dr. Isabelle Margaret Little to examine Daysey and conduct a clinical work up. Dr. Little sent urine samples off to the laboratory at Oxford's Radcliffe Infirmary & County Hospital and also called in another doctor, Thomas Saxty Good, as a consultant.

The first test results back from the Radcliffe Infirmary indicated that Daysey's urine did not contain the parasites that cause African sleeping sickness, *Trypanosoma brucei* (listed as T.B.). She had a raging kidney infection, and she had high levels of bacteria that, at the time, were termed *"B. coli"* in her urine. Dr. Good, an Oxford psychiatrist who was becoming the local expert on encephalitis lethargica, quickly confirmed the tentative diagnosis of encephalitis lethargica on the basis of Daysey's physical, behavioral, and cognitive signs and symptoms, all of which fit the emerging profile for the puzzling new sleepy sickness.

Dr. Good had presented a paper to the Oxford Medical Society the previous year in which he described the range of lethargies recorded for patients, from "slight drowsiness to complete stupor," the parkinsonian "masks" that stripped their faces of emotions, the visual anomalies that caused patients to see "badly ...

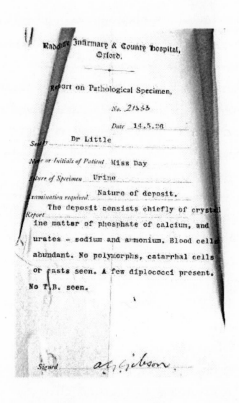

Radcliffe Infirmary & County Hospital,
Oxford.

Report on Pathological Specimen.

No. 21333

Date  14.5.26

By  Dr Little

Name or Initials of Patient  Miss Day

Nature of Specimen  Urine

Examination required  Nature of deposit.

Report  The deposit consists chiefly of crystalline matter of phosphate of calcium, and urates – sodium and ammonium. Blood cells abundant. No polymorphs, catarrhal cells or casts seen. A few diplococci present. No T.B. seen.

Signed  a. gibson.

and occasionally double," and the "hallucinations and mental confusion [and] later a tendency to depression and absolute dementia" that upset the patients' equilibria. Good stressed the importance of combining "bacteriological, anatomical, physiological and psychological" evidence in making definitive diagnoses.

He was as puzzled as were other doctors at the time about the new disease, and he urged

73

that treatments be open-minded and nuanced. "In a hospital where we are attempting to understand and treat mental illness," Good wrote, "it seems to us obvious that the factor we are dealing with is a dynamic energy not to be understood by physical examination only. We cannot see it any more than we can see electricity."

Like von Economo, Good was attempting to understand the new disease through a combination of behavioral observations, laboratory tests, and autopsy findings. He sensed that encephalitis lethargica was due to "an acute toxaemia," but he had no idea what the nature of the toxic agent might be.

Encephalitis lethargica was a complete conundrum, and it was providing physicians with a daunting therapeutic challenge. One British physician, who also spoke before the Oxford Medical Society in 1925, commented that the insomnia associated with encephalitis lethargica was, in his experience, the hardest of all insomnias to treat. His recommendation was for bedtime rituals, including recitation of Keats's Ode to Sleep.

As soon as Daysey's father arrived in Oxford, Dr. Little asked him for permission to remove Daysey's infected kidney. But George felt it was pointless to subject his daughter to surgery, because there was not the slightest hope that she would ever recover from this disease, which he knew from his reading to be invariably fatal. Let her have her last days free from the additional stress of a risky operation, he reasoned, and his decision had been final.

On May 20, 1926, George filled out "reception papers," as did Dr. Little and Dr. Good, so that Daysey could be admitted to the Warneford Psychiatric Hospital. Each declared that Daysey was "a person of unsound mind." How George felt associating those heartbreaking words with his once-brilliant, first-born daughter is unimaginable.

George also filled out a "Statement of Particulars" listing Daysey's age, sex, occupation, the duration of her illness, its suspected cause, whether she was dangerous, whether close relatives were insane, whether she had epilepsy or was suicidal, and so on. In answer to the question "When and where previously under Care and Treatment as a Lunatic, Idiot, or person of unsound mind," George wrote "Nowhere, never, nowhere."

Dr. Little and Dr. Good each filled out a "Certificate of Medical Practitioner." These included narrative sections in which each doctor

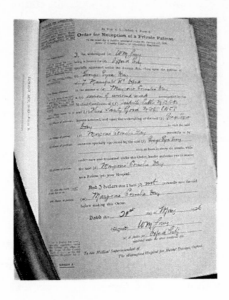

described Daysey's condition at the time of examination.

Dr. Little wrote the following comments:

*Patient states that she is being held down in bed, that she is in great pain owing to being 'pinned together,' that she hears people being torn to pieces and that their burned flesh is put over her body by her nurses; that she is given poison acids to drink and things which always cut her. Nurse Winifred Giles of the Acland Home, Oxford, at present living at 7 Mansfield Road, states that patient is at times very restless and agitated and confused in mind, thinking that she is being subjected to Caesarean section – that she is being poisoned in food which therefore she refuses – and thinking constantly that she has shot or murdered people.*

Dr. Good wrote something similar:

*She is quite confused. Has no conception of time. Has no control emotionally and is impulsive in her actions. She does not recognise persons she has seen frequently, calling them by names that are not their own. Has a delusion that she is pregnant and being cut up. Nurse Emma Wringfield of the Acland Home, attending at night to the said M.C. Day, stated that the patient states there are snakes in the bed (this is contrary to fact). Patient has stated she had shot someone and sees the body in the corner of the room.*

In the "History Prior to Admission" section of the medical record, Daysey's recent medical history was described this way:

*Came as student to Oxford last September. She had a form of influenza about Xmas. She went to Penzance for Easter vacation but it was cold and wet and she did not improve. About three weeks ago she developed acute symptoms, becoming agitated, excited, confused, mistaking identities, having delusions about pregnancy and V.D., refusing food and having insomnia. She had dysphagia about this time: Dr. Little says for two days or so she was unable to swallow. She had retention of urine followed by hematuria [urine in the blood], and a huge mass containing crystals of calcium phosphate, sodium, and ammonium crystals and abundant blood cells were passed. Culture of coliform organisms was obtained. The hematuria continued. She has had appendectomy in the past. Has had a low blood pressure and abnormal temperature for some time past. Slight dysmenorrhea [painful menstruation]. Catamenea [menstruation] otherwise normal. Agitated, confused, and suspicious. She was diagnosed before admission as a case of encephalitis lethargica.*

Tucked into the Warneford papers were fifteen small slips of paper reporting on the findings of periodic blood and urine lab tests and cell counts. Daysey never saw her medical charts, and she knew little or nothing about the early days, weeks, months and even years of her illness. But everyone else knew from the start, as did that university registrar, that Daysey had been diagnosed with encephalitis lethargica.

## 1926
## Warneford Psychiatric Hospital

Daysey was moved as a "stretcher case" (her words) from the house at Mansfield Road to the Warneford Hospital, where she remained for thirty months. (My neighbor, Emily, had told me that George had taken Daysey home right away, but he had not.). The Warneford was a private psychiatric hospital less than three miles from the center of Oxford but worlds away from the university's rich intellectual life.

The Warneford was founded in the early 1800s to serve "distressed gentlefolk," those who were neither rich enough to afford private psychiatric care at home nor so poor that they qualified for free care at the public Littlemore Hospital, the hospital headed by Dr. Thomas Saxty Good. By 1926, when Daysey was admitted to the Warneford, the hospital's one hundred patients--roughly half women and half men—were not distressed gentlefolk but members of reasonably well-off families.

The Warneford's main building was a somewhat daunting, Jacobethan-style structure. But inside, the comfortable drawing, dining, and recreation rooms fit with the hospital's therapeutic strategy, which was to offer patients as home-like a setting as possible. Even the staircase banisters, ending with wooden curlicues, were designed to resemble what patients were likely to see in their own homes. Such familiar architectural touches were thought to be helpful in promoting feelings of safety and security in the patients.

The hospital grounds stretched over one hundred and fifty acres. In Daysey's era, the campus included lovely gardens, huge chestnut trees, an orchard, and a productive dairy farm. In the summers, the grounds were alive with cricket matches, croquet and tennis games, and garden parties. An "automated house telephone" was installed in 1926, the year the hospital celebrated its centenary and the year that Daysey arrived. That summer, lavish festivities marked the big anniversary, but Daysey was unaware of any of them.

### From the Warneford medical chart
### May 21, 1926

*She is very agitated and confused, refusing food, & very suspicious of a glass of water. Her tongue is thickly coated, she has stomatitis [inflamed mucous membranes in her mouth] & sordes [crusty sores on her lips and teeth]. She is emaciated. Physical exam: resisted but no abnormality detected in chest except heart sounds being weak and rapid. A rash on chest of a septicemic character. Hair & eyes dark, pupils moderately dilated, but further exam resisted.*

### May 22

*She did not sleep last night. She fears the room or persons standing near the bed are going to fall on her. No tremors. No muscular rigidity. Slight strabismus [crossing] of right eye. Tachycardia [rapid heart rate].*

**May 23**

*After hypodermic of morphine, she had about 3 1/2 hours sleep. Confused & emotional, but coherent. She is slightly confused but replies intelligently to questions. Slight vomiting after taking medicine.*

**May 24**

*She had about 7 hours' natural sleep last night.*

**May 26**

*She continues to be agitated & confused at times. Slight hematuria [signs of blood in the urine] continues. Physical condition improved.*

**May 27**

*She had a few hours' natural sleep. She takes a little liquid food with much coaxing, eats fruit freely. Tachycardia.*

**Letter to Miss Burrows from the minister of the Oxford Presbyterian Church.**

*May 26, 1926*
*Dear Miss Burrows,*

*I was very sorry to be out when you kindly called on Saturday. It is extremely good of you to have written. ...*

*I saw Miss Day's father again yesterday. He*

*thinks that on the whole she is a little better, though still very seriously ill. I think she is in good hands in the Warneford and her father seems very well satisfied with the place.*

*Yours sincerely,*
*D.C. Lusk*

## From the medical chart
## May 28  Medical Statement

*She is agitated, confused & emotional, but has periods when she is clear & coherent. She was in a very confused state on admission which was chiefly due to the large amount of [indecipherable: some drug] she had prior to admission. She suspects poison in her food which she will take only after much persuasion. She has delusions, saying the nurses are going to cut her in pieces, or that the walls of her room will fall on her. She has cystitis [inflammation of the bladder] with hematuria. The urine also shows B. Coli, triple phosphates, staphylococci & pus-cells. She is very emaciated; had a slight strabismus of right eye on admission; her heart is very weak & rapid in action.*

## May 30

*She stated that a fire took place in this hospital last night which was a delusion. Taking more liquid food. Urine contains fewer B. Coli and staphylococci & is no longer blood coloured.*

**May 31**
*She slept about 3 1/2 hours in all during night. Quiet for the most part but very deluded.*

Throughout that May and into June, George watched as his daughter lay lifeless and unconscious for hours at a time, then sometimes acted out, screamed, or babbled nonsense. He sent short, pithy cables home every day to Ella and Marion—"no change" or "chins up."

He combed the university and the town of Oxford, searching for possible explanations for how Daysey might have contracted this fatal encephalitis, but he found no clues anywhere. He questioned Daysey's friends and acquaintances and university officials. The disease was considered highly contagious, yet no one else was sick, not even the close friends who had been with Daysey in Penzance. Daysey noted in her memoir that George actually did investigate the possibility that her illness was African sleeping sickness and that larvae of the tsetse fly had somehow been brought into England in some foreign student's luggage, but his research yielded nothing.

**From the medical chart**
**June 2**
*As she has taken very little liquid food or drink &*
*urine was scanty, she was tube-fed with eggs & milk.*

**June 7**
*She had 7 3/4 hours sleep (after paraldehyde &*
*[indecipherable: some chemical drug]) last night &*
*looks better. [Blood and urine analyses show]*
*organisms & other abnormal constituents as before*
*but much diminished.*

**June 9**
*Proportion of lymphocytes slightly in excess of*
*normal.*

**June 10**
*3 1/2 hours sleep last night. Tube-fed twice daily.*
*Slight improvement in bodily condition. She is*
*quieter.*

**June 11**
*At her father's request & on his responsibility, 2 c.c. of*
*sterilized milk was injected intramuscularly in left*
*thigh this evening.*

## June 16

*9 hours' sleep. Blood pressure: systolic 130; diastolic 95. She stammers a few broken words over & over again.*

Many weeks passed and Daysey continued to be unaware of her surroundings and of her father's presence at her side. Then, suddenly, one day, for one brief moment, she emerged from her "feverish unconsciousness" and recognized her father's hand on her wrist, taking her pulse.

She vividly recalled that June incident. She described hearing George's familiar voice.

"Yes, dear, this is your daddy," George said. "Here, eat this!" and he spooned a bit of melon into her mouth.

But that was it. Darkness closed around her once again, and she quickly lapsed back into her netherworld.

Only infrequently over the next ten years did Daysey have moments of awareness like that one. Whenever she woke up, she saw that she was in a strange place, lying in a bed or on a stretcher, and attended by white-clad figures. Her immediate assumption was that she was in prison and that the white-clad figures were jailers. But why she was incarcerated was always a mystery and, in any case, was of little or no interest to her.

**Letter from Wellesley's president, Miss Ellen Pendleton, to Miss Burrows, the principal of the Oxford Society of Home Students.**

*June 17, 1926*
*My dear Miss Burrows,*

*Please pardon me for not having replied earlier to your very kind letter of May 19th. I had learned of Miss Day's serious illness from her family, but I appreciate very much your letter with its additional details. We are all very greatly saddened by Miss Day's illness, and we still have a faint hope that she may ultimately recover, although we realize how long any possible convalescence will be.*

*I hope that I may see you in Amsterdam this summer.*

*I am most sincerely yours,*
*Ellen F. Pendleton*

**From the medical chart**
**June 18**
*9 hours' sleep with sedatives.*

**June 21  Report at end of month**
*She is confused, agitated & distressed. She says only a few stammering words, which she repeats without*

*completing. She has delusions of poison & torture. She refuses all food & drink & has to be tube-fed. She has severe pyelo-nephritis [kidney infection], organisms found being B. coli & staphylococci. She is emaciated, her heart is weak in action & liable to frequent attacks of tachycardia. Her condition has been very serious since admission.*

## June 23

*She has 7 to 9 hours sleep after sedatives. Tube-feeding is satisfactory. Her general condition is improved. Mental condition unchanged.*

## June 24

*Dr. Little, her former medical attendant, saw the patient today and thought her much improved.*

**Letter from Daysey's sister, Marion, to Miss Burrows, principal of the Oxford Home Students.**

*June 26, 1926*
*My dear Miss Burrows,*

*My mother and I wish to thank you for your many kindnesses to my sister Marjorie and for your message to us.*

*Ever since we received the first word of Marjorie's illness we believed that every care was given her. It has been very comforting to have your*

*letters and so understand a bit of her health history for
these past few months.*

*We, here, feel far away, yet so grateful to you,
and the friends who have been with Marjorie. While
awaiting news of any development and anxiously
hoping for encouraging word, we think of those who
have helped her, and shall always remember your
interest and kindness.*

*Sincerely,*
*Marion L. Day*

Miss Burrows was doing all that she
could think to do to help the family endure the
awful ordeal. Occasionally, she would invite
George to join her and her mother for dinner.
George was an entertaining guest, despite his
troubles, and she could see where Daysey had
gotten her energy and her self confidence.

George expressed strong opinions. One
night he talked about how he found Lloyd
George to be a "tricky opportunist" and how he
thought the leader of a recent coal strike "would
better be hanged." He was ashamed of his own
countrymen, whom, he thought, had been too
slow to join the war effort, leaving England to
"sacrifice the flower of your land for four long
years" before receiving any American aid.
George talked about the Americans he

admired — New York's governor Al Smith, Mississippi's U.S. senator Blanche Bruce (the first African American to be elected a U.S. Senator), Columbia University's president Nicholas Butler (who was also a Nobel Peace Prize winner), Teddy Roosevelt, and Abe Lincoln, "a rail splitter possessed of fine qualities." He prided himself on the fact that his paternal grandmother was "pure English," and he hoped that the "true sportsmanship" of the English character had somehow become part of his own blood. He called himself a "renegade American" and seemed pleased with the moniker he had chosen.

## From the medical chart
### June 30
*She had a restless night and today has attacks of struggling and resistance, springing up in bed & moaning about wrong she has done & the torture of her mother and sister.*

### July 3
*She has been having more sleep. Tachycardia & slight rise of temperature (99.8 or thereabouts) at times. Urine clear, no albumin, not offensive.*

### July 8
*10 1/2 hours sleep yesterday altogether. She is more*

demented, making usually a low whimpering &
whining noise & only occasionally articulating words
with difficulty.

### July 19

Urine is now clear, with very few cells to be seen,
slight trace of albumin. Her mental condition has
improved the last few days. She recollects more, and at
intervals talks quite rationally.

### July 22

She averages 8 or 9 hours sleep each night with
sedatives. She talks of horrors: cruelty to children &
animals, white slave traffic, & continually refers to her
sister, whom she thinks is going to be tortured. She
will only take a few sips of milk-food naturally.

### Aug 1

She has had 8-10 hours sleep each night with
sedatives. She gets up now each day and walks in
garden, and has eaten some bread & butter & fruit.
Shouts & screams at times.

### Aug 5

She has eaten two meals and is clearer in her
conversation.

**Aug 6**

*She has taken food naturally & is clearer & only excited & noisy at times. On one occasion she conversed quite rationally for a short time.*

**Aug 15**

*As urine was scanty & she was taking little fluid, she was tube-fed with plenty of fluid this afternoon.*

George stayed on in Oxford for three heart-breaking months. His presence there failed, however, to bring about noticeable improvements in his daughter's condition. He spoke daily with Daysey's doctors and nurses, and he felt comforted that at least she was receiving scrupulous medical and nursing care.

In August, George gave up his vigil and headed home, sailing from Southampton port on the passenger liner Carmania. A friend and neighbor from home, Robert Groh, had commented to his own daughter (one of the people I interviewed) when George left for Oxford, "It's going to be a long trip," and, indeed, Groh had been right.

**From the medical chart**
**Aug 23**

*She continues to be very distressed & agitated at*

*times, talking of horrible things happening.*

**Sept 6**
*She continues to be confused & disoriented, & agitated & depressed.*

**Sept 20**
*No mental improvement. She is at times confused, dull & unresponsive.*

**Oct 19**
*She continues very confused & dull. More demented in expression & carriage. Eats voraciously.*

**October letter to George from Dr. Neill of the Warneford Hospital.**

*Dear Dr. Day,*

*We regret to tell you that yesterday, after a more extensive brain exploration in your daughter's case, we found that the destruction of brain areas is more extensive than we had determined while you were here. She has no pupillary reflex, no knee jerk. She remains completely disoriented.*

By November, Daysey's sister and mother—Marion and Ella—had moved to Oxford to take up the vigil. Daysey's situation was not looking good, but they wanted to be with her in case she might begin to recover or might experience other moments of clarity like the one that George had witnessed.

Each day they donned face masks and helped the nurses with Daysey's care. But Daysey was never conscious of their presence at the hospital. She remained isolated in her bubble of confusion, making absolutely no connections with the people around her and having no awareness of her condition.

She did, though, later recall certain delusions that began during her Warneford stay and continued to plague her for many years.

The first was that she had committed a grisly crime. Otherwise, why was she perpetually incarcerated and sometimes tied down and always supervised by white-coated jailers? (She actually had been tied to her bed at times early in her illness to protect her from injuring herself during her "raving stages.") As to the nature of her grievous crime: she had no idea.

The second delusion was that several inmates of this 'jail' were being executed each day. Every morning, Daysey watched from her perch on the hospital's screened sunporch as the day's "victims" filed across a tidy grassy area and into the small stone building that stood on the other side of the spiky iron fence. Then, ominous noises issued from the building as the "death machinery" ground up those whose day to die had come. She, too, was doomed to die, she knew, although, in her case, there was to be no grinding machinery.

And that was her third delusion. She was doomed to die by impalement.

"I am supposed to get out of this bed and impale myself on those iron points," Daysey recalled thinking. "When I do that, all will be over." She did not fear dying in that way nor did she consider that such a death would involve intense suffering. She was simply puzzled: how could she raise herself from the bed to do it? She was unable to walk, she was always carried on a stretcher from place to place (this was what she believed, although her medical chart indicated that she was walking on her own), so how could she possibly make her own way to that fence with its spikes?

Years later, when Daysey took a sentimental journey back to Oxford and out to the Warneford, she found that the building she had seen across the way was the hospital's small Church of England chapel, not an execution chamber. She realized that the women who had filed into it each morning were not those slated to die but nurses, and the "grinding, piercing" noises that she thought she heard were simply the voices of the congregants as they sang their morning hymns.

The daily extermination had what Daysey described as "yet other insane features. I believed the victims to be farm workers and milkmaids. I thought the daily death march involved two or three of these people going to their deaths each day. I heard the jangle of pans somewhere in this jail, and, in my distorted mind, that noise came from milk pails. We all had to go, the executioners did their grim work gradually, and there was no escape."

Long after Daysey was well, she told Marion about these fantasies. Marion was astonished when Daysey described the executioner--the one with the "distinctive, flowing head-dress and a threatening voice with a witch's cackle." Marion recognized in this description the chief supervising nurse of the hospital, a woman to whom she had grown extremely close, a "soft-voiced Scotswoman who was known for her professional devotion and kindness."

Thoughts of death haunted Daysey not just during the day time but at night as well. She recalled lying in her bed, watching the leaping flames in the log fireplace, and thinking, "Somehow I am supposed to get from this bed into the flames and vanish up the chimney. But how can I get from here to the fireplace when I can't walk?"

**From the medical chart**
**Nov 12**
*Dr. Thomas Saxty Good today examined the patient in consultation with Dr. Neill & wrote appended report.*

Ruth Levy Guyer

*I to-day examined Miss Day in consultation with Dr. Neill at the Warneford Hospital. <u>Physically</u>. I found her fairly well nourished, and less anemic than when I last examined her. She however showed rather a mask-like expression and her pupils were moderately dilated. They reacted to light and to accommodation. The upper reflexes appeared to be normal, but there was some exaggeration of both knee-jerks, and there was a definite extensor reaction of both plantars. The heart's action was fairly good but the sounds were muffled. The control of the bladder and rectum appeared to be sometimes lost. She is taking food fairly well and is sleeping better. The urine now appears to be clearer, and as I understand at present is free from casts which previously had been present. <u>Mentally</u>. There was no sign of any recognition nor could I get any reply to any question, and there was no sign of any emotion. From a conversation I had with her sister, it appears that for some little time past, it is only very old associations which appear to be understood, and she does not appear capable of recognizing objects around her. From the symptoms that I observed, I fear that there is very grave mischief of an organic character in the brain, almost certainly in the cortical area. This supposition is borne out by the fact that there is a good deal of hypertonicity and rigidity of the muscles, especially in the lower limbs. I am afraid that the prognosis is extremely grave, and it is extremely* *doubtful as to whether she would ever recover, even partially. Her temperature at present is extremely variable, and from an examination of the charts from the time of her admission to the present date there are indications that there is and has been a strong toxicity. She appears to me to have been excellently nursed and everything to have been done that was possible. Her mental condition is such that psycho-therapy could not be used as she is quite alienated from the world of reality. In my opinion, she is a case that is quite unsuitable for treatment outside a mental hospital, and I am further of the opinion that it would be a great mistake at the present time to have her removed, both from a physical and a mental point of view.*

*T.S. Good*

### 1927   From the medical chart
**Jan 1**
*No change in mind. She continues to be very dull & listless, & only speaks occasionally & then of delusions.*

**Feb 20**
*There are occasional flashes of recollection, but she soon becomes apathetic again.*

**Mar 8**

*Occasional periods of recollection occur. The Reverend Lusk, her minister, after visiting her today, reported the patient took some intelligent interest in his conversation and prayers, and made appropriate remarks.*

**Letter from Daysey's father, George E. Day, to Oxford Home Students' principal, Miss Burrows.**

*April 24, 1927*
*Dear Miss Burrows,*

*Nearly a year has passed since I sailed for England on my sad mission. However I shall always remember your kindnesses to Marjorie, Marion and myself. ...*

*As you know poor Marjorie does not improve and can not, as encephalitis is a progressive disease. I believe the best I can do is to keep the dear child at Warneford, especially as long as Miss Richardson and Miss McGeorge [the matrons of the hospital at the time] are there, as I have the utmost faith in their trustworthiness and goodness of heart.*

*As Marjorie does not even recognize Marion and she brings no solace or comfort to her, I have written Marion that she may as well come home, for a time at least.*

*With many kind wishes for your self and your sweet mother believe me*

*Sincerely yours,*
*Geo. E. Day*

**From the medical chart**
**Apr 29  Special Report**
*She is quiet & abstracted, dull & apathetic, but at times becoming agitated & distressed. She is very confused & continues to have delusions about poison & torture. She takes her food well now & her physical condition is greatly improved.*

**Apr 30**
*She was taken out for a short drive by her sister today, but was miserable, talking about poisons, etc.*

**May 28**
*She has brighter intervals at times during which she shows more intelligence.*

**Jul 5  Physical Exam**
*Heart: strong & normal. She walks in a tired hesitating way & has to be urged along. Tongue slightly coated. Eats & sleeps well. When taken for a drive in Oxford the other day she pointed out the different colleges to her sister. She still reverts at times*

to her complaints of "something terrible happening."
Menstruation has returned after a long absence.

**Aug 11**

She continues to have brighter intervals, during
which she smiles & shows interest, but soon reverts to
apathy.

**Oct 26  Physical Exam**

No abnormalities detected. Knee-jerks exaggerated.

**Nov 16**

She is miserable in expression, with a hunted, scared
look. Continually repeats "I do love my mother" or "I
have never done any dirty things." Eats & sleeps
fairly.

**1928**

**Feb 27**

There is little change in her mental condition. Her
expression is happier on the whole, & she shows brief
flashes of intelligence but soon relapses, & continues
repeating sentences disclaiming bad behavior in the
past. Her physical condition is fair.

**Apr 6**

Her habits at table are very repulsive.

**Apr 26  Special Report**

*She is very confused & still has delusions about torture & poisons. She is usually dull & apathetic, but at times becomes agitated, continually repeating some sentence such as "I do love my mother," or "There is something terrible happening." She is clumsy & repulsive in her manners at table & is at times wet & dirty. She is now in good bodily health & condition.*

**May 20**

*No mental or physical change to record. Faulty habits.*

**Jun 20**

*Patient is becoming more demented.*

**Jul 20**

*No change to record. Habits most degraded & faulty.*

A few American friends visited Daysey while she was at the Warneford, but she never recognized any of them. One of these was the Wellesley professor, Mary Whiton Calkins, who chaired the psychology-philosophy department, had supervised Daysey's Master of Arts research, and had encouraged Daysey to pursue her studies of neo-realism in Oxford. Miss Calkins said to a friend on her return to the States, "Poor Marjorie Day. That good brain of hers is being burned up cell by cell by that horrible disease."

Daysey's mother, Ella, was completely devastated. She went to the hospital day after day for months on end, but Daysey never once recognized her. In despair, Ella sailed home on the Mauritania from Southampton on August 4, 1928. She disembarked at New York, where George met her and drove her back home to Strasburg.

Marion stayed on in Oxford. She never left her sister's side, even when her father suggested she take a break. For some reason, she always remained hopeful, even though she never saw signs of progress.

Soon after Ella returned home, she and George began talking about moving Daysey back to the United States. It would be best for the family, they felt, to have their daughter near them so they could watch over her as her illness evolved.

They wrote a letter to the doctors in Oxford describing their plan and received the following assessment back from them:

**Letter from Oxford doctors, Good and Neill, to Daysey's parents.**

*August 14, 1928*

*I have had a consultation with Dr. Neill at the Warneford Hospital, and very carefully examined Miss M. Day, and I find that physically she is not improved. The reflexes are still unequal on the two sides, and there is loss of control over the rectum and bladder, and in spite of most careful feeding she is losing weight. Mentally she is confused, and is quite incapable of thinking in terms of time, place or person, that is to say, she confuses one person with another, and does not realise where she is.*

*Her condition is I am afraid in-curable, and she requires constant nursing and observation both night and day. She is in such a condition she could not be moved, or go on a journey unless she had two trained nurses, as she is not fit to be left. Although I understand you wish to remove her to America, no reputable shipping company could take her without two trained nurses in attendance.*

*It would be quite impossible for any who are not trained nurses to adequately look after your daughter. It would not be safe from the patient's point of view, and also would be a great strain on the people who were in charge of her, it would in addition, inflict unnecessary suffering on her to be improperly looked after.*

*If therefore it is your wish to have her removed to America, I can only emphasize the facts that no company would transship her without two trained nurses accompanying her, and it is also our considered opinion that it would be very inadvisable, if not impossible to attempt to nurse her in a private house.*

> *Thos. S. Good,*
> *Medical Superintendent, Littlemore*
> *Alex. W. Neill,*
> *Medical Superintendent,*
> *The Warneford*

## From the medical chart
### Sep 17
*She has been getting thinner lately.*

### Sep 26
*Teeth, tongue & breath very foul. Antiseptic mouthwash ordered.*

### Oct 2
*Creps [crepitations or crackling sounds] heard indistinctly at both apices (tips of the lungs), but exam very difficult owing to patient's constant talking.*

### Oct 10
*Her mental condition remains unaltered.*

**Oct 31**

*By direction of petitioner she was today discharged. She was taken today by car to Southhampton in charge of two nurses. Her sister met her there, & the following day patient is to sail in S.S. "George Washington" in charge of her sister & two nurses for New York, where her father will meet her.*

    *Discharged*

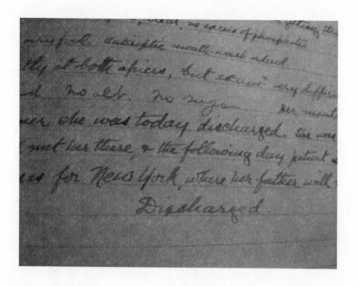

# 1928

## The Journey Home

Daysey had not died from her 'fatal' encephalitis lethargica. Nor had she recovered. She appeared to be suspended in a kind of limbo, permanently gripped in the disease's terrible stranglehold.

No one could predict how much longer Daysey might live and continue to need institutional care. But, with Daysey closer to home, George and Ella felt that they and Marion might be able to resume some semblance of their own 'normal' lives.

George asked Marion to arrange for the passage back to the United States. As the doctors wrote in their letter to the Days, they were still under the impression that Daysey's disease was dangerous to others.

Marion hired two nurses for round-the-clock duty on the ship and reserved a set of staterooms in which the four travelers could remain sequestered during their journey across the Atlantic. The ship's doctor agreed to participate in Daysey's care as needed, and the ship's kitchen staff agreed to serve the group their meals in their rooms.

These arrangements had taken some time and effort to orchestrate, and, in fact, Marion succeeded only after the American ambassador in London had intervened. The ship's authorities at first objected to transporting an incurable and dangerously ill patient. This was not the usual business of the big ocean liners, although they did occasionally do it. For example, two years earlier, the New York Times had reported on the arrival back in the United States of the winner of the British amateur golf tournament, who was "removed in a stretcher from the Aquitania at Quarantine and taken to the Lawrence Hospital in a private ambulance." The famous American golfer was not, like Daysey, suffering from encephalitis lethargica but had after effects of influenza.

On November 1, 1928, Daysey, Marion and the two nurses set sail on the S.S. George Washington from the port at Southampton. The journey took twelve days.

The George Washington was a massive German liner, built in 1908. It left Bremerhaven for the first time in 1909. The ship's décor — walls

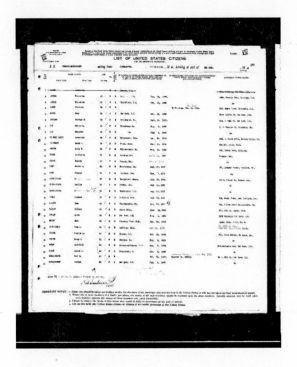

painted with giant murals depicting events in George Washington's life—and even the ship's name had been strategic: the manufacturer wanted the German passengers who were sailing from their homeland to America to feel optimistic about their chances of being accepted in the United States.

In 1914, when the war began, the ship happened to be docked in New York. There it stayed until the United States entered the war. The U.S. Navy converted the ship to a troop ship and, from 1917 until the war ended, the George

Washington crisscrossed the ocean, ferrying soldiers to Europe and bringing decommissioned and injured soldiers home. The masthead of the ship's wartime newspaper--*The Hatchet*--boasted that the publication had "The Largest Circulation on the Atlantic Ocean," substantiating the claim with its own version of George Washington's motto, "We Cannot Tell a Lie."

After the war, the George Washington was retrofitted to sail again as a passenger ship but, this time, with a U.S. flag. (During the Second World War, the George Washington was again commandeered as a military vessel.)

The incarnation of the ship that Daysey, Marion, and the nurses sailed on was luxurious. The three thousand passengers enjoyed a gym, a solarium, an open air cafe, dog kennels run by a kennel master, a dark room, smoking rooms, reading rooms, and so on. The plush dining rooms served hundreds of guests at each seating. At various times, royalty, U.S. presidents, renowned writers, Vanderbilts, Gettys, and members of other prominent families sailed on the liner. The ship even ferried exotic animals from India—lions, elephants, monkeys and chimpanzees (including one chimp named His

Darwinian Highness), peacocks, canaries—to zoos in the United States.

What exactly went on during Daysey's journey and which notables were on board that time Daysey did not know. She, her sister, and the nurses did not mingle with the other passengers or, in fact, enjoy any of the ship's amenities. They remained sequestered in their rooms.

Daysey recalled a single, snapshot image of the journey and nothing at all about the ship itself or the long voyage.

"I remember loud blasts of ear-splitting noise as I lay on a stretcher somewhere. I remember scurrying feet and confusing darkness. My sister later suggested that this must have been the Southampton dock where we waited to board the liner."

In those days, Southampton was a bustling trans-Atlantic seaport, home port for not just the S.S. George Washington but also the two famous Cunard liners—the Queen Mary and the Queen Elizabeth. Decades earlier, Southampton had been the embarkation point for the Titanic on its ill-fated maiden journey, and, three hundred years before that, the Mayflower had set sail from there for the United States.

When the S.S. George Washington steamed into New York harbor on November 12, 1928, George and Ella were waiting at the dock, and so was an ambulance. Passengers disembarked into the open arms of their loved ones. Cheers went up from the crowd as families were reunited. Then, Marion and the nurses walked together down the gangplank, accompanied by their "stretcher case." Daysey was quickly transferred off the gurney and into the ambulance, which drove her directly to Philadelphia, Pennsylvania.

## 1928
## Pennsylvania Hospital

George had made arrangements for Daysey to be cared for at Pennsylvania Hospital, an elite psychiatric facility in Philadelphia, just a few hours east of Strasburg. He knew a rising-star psychiatrist at the hospital, Kenneth Appel, who had grown up in Lancaster and had been a childhood friend of both of his daughters. (Kenneth had actually dated Marion for a brief time, and he and Marion and Daysey had all gone to dances together in their teenage days.) By 1928, Kenneth Appel was the head of Pennsylvania Hospital's neurology department, and George was comforted to know that Kenneth would supervise Daysey's care on the ward.

Daysey recalled very few memories of her first seven-year stay at the Pennsylvania Hospital.

The first clear image was from a summer's afternoon, eight months after she

114

arrived in Philadelphia. She woke up and, as usual, found herself surrounded by white-clad figures. She noticed an open newspaper lying on her bed. She reached for it and made out the large capitalized nameplate:

THE PHILADELPHIA INQUIRER
July 1929

She recalled bolting upright.

"The Philadelphia Inquirer—1929?! But I left for Oxford in 1926. Where am I? Where have I been?"

She felt immediately oriented. Had she been in an accident? Had she been kidnapped? These thoughts flashed through her mind. She felt her head: no bandages. She reached to see if her legs were there: they were. What was going on?

"Get my family," Daysey said. "My father is Dr. George Ezra Day of Strasburg. Get him quickly. Hurry."

The nurse at her bedside was patient and reassuring.

"Hush. Calm down," she said. "We know who you are. We know you were in Oxford. Your father knows that you are here.

Here, drink this," the nurse said, and she thrust a bent straw between Daysey's lips.

Loud, disturbing noises came through the open window. Pandemonium, Daysey thought, although the sounds were simply those of downtown Philadelphia's city traffic.

Somehow Daysey knew that her awareness would be brief. In a few minutes she lapsed off again, closing in once more.

"That breathtaking moment of wakefulness, my grasp of reality," noted Daysey, "was quickly over."

Days at the Pennsylvania Hospital grew into weeks, then dissolved into months and years.

At some point, part of the therapeutic plan was to increase Daysey's mobility. Thus, one morning, the attending nurse dressed Daysey, helped her stand up, and then began to slowly lead her out of her room into the hallway. This was the first time that Daysey was aware of having gotten out of bed or off a stretcher and taking steps on her own.

A full-length mirror hung in the hallway. As Daysey emerged from her room on the arm of the nurse, she saw her image in the glass. A chilling shock went through her. Gray hair! A haggard, aged face! Discolored teeth! Me?? That hag?

"Take me back to bed," Daysey commanded. She wanted nothing to do with the ravaged apparition who gaped at her from the mirror.

Soon, though, her ability to walk ably and independently returned permanently, and after that she remembers the monotony of endless, empty days, walking from her room to the day room, sitting there with the other psychiatric patients, going on daily strolls through the hospital grounds, always accompanied by white-uniformed staff and the other patients.

For some time she continued to believe that she was in jail, but eventually that delusion vanished. She now vaguely became aware of being in a hospital, and she began to recognize the white-uniformed people who were always around her as nurses.

Still, she felt captive. She had no idea why she had to be in a hospital, and she deeply resented the freedom of the nurses and doctors, who came and went as they pleased.

In the day room, the nurses would invariably hand her magazines, which she could not read, because all of the words ran together.

She remembered thinking that her "keepers" must never know that she couldn't read. So, she would leaf through the magazines, pretending to be absorbed in the stories. She would look at the pictures of movie stars, knowing that their names, had she been able to read them, would mean nothing to her. Daysey had been a huge fan of the live theater and of certain actors, Julia Marlowe, Ann Sothern, John Drew, Otis Skinner, Sarah Bernhardt, and the Barrymores. She especially loved Mrs. Fiske, whom she had often gone to see in *Salvation Nell*. The new "silent films" had never been of interest to her.

The Pennsylvania Hospital's treatment regimen included numerous injections, which Daysey thought were probably tranquilizers. She came to resent the never-ending needles, and the "sneaky" way in which the nurses would come, sit amiably by her side on one of the long settees in the hallway, and then, without warning, stab her arm.

The only time that staff members would forewarn her about a procedure was when they needed to withdraw blood or inject it. A doctor would arrive holding a terrifyingly long transfusion needle. Two or three nurses would hold her down on her bed, and the intravenous piercing would begin. She dreaded and despised the ignominy of those forced transactions and resented the big "horse" needles, which were exactly like the ones that the veterinarian in Strasburg had used on her father's horses when she was a child.

She described the staff members as "unrelenting" in their attempts to start conversations with her and evoke emotional reactions. They would come into her room, sit down beside her, and begin:

"So, you used to go to Oxford," a staff member might say.

But Daysey always made sure that the conversations went nowhere. She remained extremely uncooperative, making only perfunctory and rude replies: "I don't want to hear about that" or "That was another life. I'm here now." Years later, Marion confirmed that Daysey was characterized at the hospital as "a very uncooperative patient."

Seared deepest in her memory from her first years in the Pennsylvania Hospital was an incident that took place on the sultry summer evening of July 10, 1930. She was lying quietly in her room, when in walked a young doctor Daysey did not recognize. He was dressed in a tuxedo, ready, she presumed, to go out and enjoy himself after completing his evening rounds.

He began with the usual question, "How are you?" And then he casually said, "You know, your father died yesterday. Died of a heart attack."

"No," Daysey replied. "I didn't know."

"Yes, heart condition, you know. He came here often to see you — a very fine doctor."

Was this some sort of ruse? Daysey wondered. Was this doctor testing her so that he could write "Patient showed little emotion" on the chart for his evening report? Soon, the young doctor departed, and Daysey spent a troubled night wondering about what he had said, hoping that her father was alive, but, really, how could she know? There was just enough truth in the doctor's shocking disclosure for it to be authentic. She knew that, when she had left for Oxford, her father had been diagnosed with "a slight coronary condition," although, as far as she knew, he had never had an actual heart attack.

Early the next day, Marion, whom she now often recognized, entered her room. Daysey gave Marion one look and said, "Daddy? Is it true?" Daysey said she never forgot the shocked, sad look on Marion's face as she whispered,

"Yes, but who told you? I came to tell you."
Their father had paid weekly visits to Daysey in
Philadelphia, but in all those months she had
never recognized him. And now he was dead.

Daysey surmised that "the emotions of a
damaged brain are fleeting and do not seem to
cut deep," because she remembered feeling no
real reaction to the doctor's revelation--no tears,
for example—and none to Marion's confirmation
of the news, only a stunned, sullen retreat back
into her own imaginings.

Another sign of how dull Daysey's
emotions and psyche were at that time was the
fact that she never once inquired about her
mother, not when she learned of her father's
death, nor when her sister was with her, nor at
any other time. In fact, she recalled one day
sitting on a couch with a nurse, who was trying
to engage her in conversation ("hopeless, as
usual"). The nurse asked, "What about your
mother? Is she still alive?"

Daysey's answer was, "I don't know. I
hope so." She said she had never thought about
her mother one way or the other, although she
and her mother had always been extremely
close.

Years afterward, Daysey learned that her
mother had stayed away from the Pennsylvania

Hospital on George's advice. Ella had been completely traumatized in Oxford, visiting Daysey every day for weeks on end without Daysey ever recognizing her. The nurse's question was the first reminder Daysey had that she actually had a mother.

Daysey wrote, "It took the dreadful snake pit of a big state mental hospital to which I was later sent to arouse in me any emotional reactions."

Daysey was declared, after seven years in the Pennsylvania Hospital, to be a chronically ill patient with little or no hope of recovery. Thus, Kenneth Appel's elite mental-care department could no longer justify keeping her in Philadelphia, and so she was moved to a large state psychiatric facility about one hundred miles from Strasburg.

She did not recall the actual trip to the state hospital, but she never forget what she experienced there—the sights, the sounds, the incivility of the huge, impersonal barracks. The indignities of her treatment in that "warehouse" somehow got through her mask of numbness. The daily routine was insulting and degrading. But there, at last, she began to feel an emotion deeply, the emotion of disgust. Finally, she became aware of her environment, and she began responding to it.

## 1936

## Warehoused

In 1936, ten years after her illness began, Daysey became a reluctant member of a "pack" of hundreds of women warehoused by the state of Pennsylvania. Three times a day, the women were marched to the dining room en masse. As a pack, they were paraded to the doorless bathrooms whenever the guards commanded "all out to the toilets," and they were herded back to their ward at night. Their beds consisted of a thin mattress, a thick red rubber sheet, and a coarse blanket. That was all.

The day began for the women with a five-minute community shower. The pack members stood in open stalls, and the attendants turned on a heavy blast of water and hosed down the row of naked women. Next, the women filed into the clothing room, where the attendants tossed two pieces of clothing at each woman.

"I shall never forget those outfits, the

124

'state dresses' that we wore," Daysey wrote. The undergarment was made of unbleached muslin and resembled the one-piece "onsies" that little babies wear today. The over-garment was a shapeless, coarse, brownish-gray sack made of mattress ticking, with a "hole at the top to crawl through and long enough to reach to every woman's ankles, no matter what her height might be."

Each person grabbed two "state shoes" from a pile on the floor of the clothing room. Daysey always hoped to at least get one right and one left shoe. She guessed that these were surplus "over-sized workingmen's shoes," because she never succeeded in grabbing any shoes that came close to her foot size.

"We flopped around all day in those ill-fitting outfits," Daysey recalled.

After breakfast, the women were herded into the big, bleak day room with its barred windows. The room was barren except for the people: it had no books, no puzzles, no games of any kind.

Later in the morning, an attendant at the door would shout, "All out for coats." The women "scuttled" to the adjoining coat room to grab a coat from a motley heap on the floor. Marion had given Daysey a full-length camel's hair polo coat. The coat was actually hers, her possession, but each day she had to fight to claim it from the pile. Her adversary was "big fat Jessie, who had taken a fancy to the coat." Jessie usually beat Daysey to the coat, and when Daysey objected, "That's mine," Jessie would grin and reply, "I like it. It smells nice." Daysey then had to make do with "any bedraggled coat left in the pile." The attendant never intervened, probably because she, like Daysey, recognized Jessie's superior physical prowess.

The hospital's grounds were large and shaded, with expansive and stately oak trees. In good weather, Daysey would separate herself from the noisy herd and lie on the grass, alone, feeling relieved, momentarily, from the press of the others.

Most of the women in the pack were nameless, but Jessie stood out, as did a small, emaciated, black woman named Kate. Everybody knew Kate, Daysey recalled, "because she marched around the day room ceaselessly, clutching a forlorn little candy box that contained a broken comb, a cracked purse mirror, and the stub of a pencil. Kate was never still; she never sat moping or mumbling, like many of us. Always on the move, she used to march around the day room or the sleeping barracks shouting, 'Hooray for Abe Lincoln, our first pres-i-dent. Hooray for Abe Lincoln!! He set the niggers free.'"

Daysey felt that Kate was somehow luckier than most of the other women in the ward, because, after all, she "had a pocket comb, half toothless though it was."

The pack groaned and muttered and shouted obscenities. Someone was always on the move, day and night. Many ranted about their husbands, whom they blamed for packing them off to this hateful place. Daysey felt more abused than shocked by their rants, especially at night time, when the relentless noise never ceased to disturb her sleep.

The state hospital offered nothing but crude, custodial care. Never, as far as Daysey knew, did the staff give anyone a quieting drug. She remembered sometimes being roused in the night by an attendant, who would thrust a spoonful of a sweet, oily substance into her mouth and say, "Here, swallow this. You've been coughing."

On occasion, the pack would be lined up for quick and merciless dental treatments. It was in that dentist's chair that Daysey recalled experiencing actual physical cruelty. A short, blonde, white-uniformed woman, whom Daysey felt sure was a rehabilitated patient, stood on one side of the chair, forceps visible and ready. A muscular man, likely also a former patient who had been promoted to an attendant, stood on the other side. The man forcefully pinned one patient in the chair; then the woman yanked out the tooth, using no pain-deadening drugs.

The first time Daysey was subjected to one of these extractions she recalled "blood and tears, and looking into that shrewd, callous little blonde's face and muttering, 'You are the cruelest woman I have ever encountered.'" But the woman's response was pat and unsym-pathetic: "It's all in the business, dearie." Then, Daysey was pushed out of the chair, the woman shouted "next!" and another victim was shoved into place.

"We were a depersonalized horde," Daysey said. "We had no names, no identities, no real care. We were just the members of a pack."

Once or twice a week, the pack filed into a makeshift theater to watch a movie. This was the only entertainment that the hospital ever offered. Daysey clearly recalled the command, "All out to the movies," but she could not remember a single film that she saw. She did remember "the spectacle of rows of bedraggled men patients, many of them with telltale spots of dark wetness on their pants. They would leer at us from the other side of the auditorium, and they would stamp and shout applause or disapproval in response to what was happening on the silent screen."

The dreary institutional life had few dramatic moments. But, occasionally, Daysey said, "bits of action would enliven our meals. When there was anything throwable, like hard-boiled eggs or potatoes in their skins, one could expect the hurling through the air of these ready-made missiles."

Most of the time, though, the food was gruel-like and soupy. The kitchen staff wheeled huge cauldrons into the dining room and pushed them slowly down the aisle that separated the parallel rows of tables. The servers would slap a ladle of gruel onto a tin plate and then fling each plate down the long, zinc-lined tables. Ten or twelve patients sat on each side of a table, and they would each grab a plate as one slid by.

Daysey took pleasure in the arrival of the newsboy every evening at supper time. He would march down the middle aisle shouting headlines. He often repeated the name "Hitler." What she gathered from the tone of the newsboy was that this Hitler, whom she supposed must be one of the men patients, was certainly causing the institution trouble. "Good for him," Daysey thought, with vindictive pleasure, "Good for Hitler. I'm glad there is somebody here who can stand up to our heartless bosses."

One day at lunch, Daysey was sitting beside a strapping woman she had noticed before with interest, because, in appearance, with her short, coarse, black hair, bass voice, and sturdy frame, the woman looked and acted more like a man than a woman. In fact, had she not been dressed in one of the shapeless state dresses, Daysey would have thought she had escaped from the men's side of the room. She had never before spoken to this woman, but on that day the woman said to Daysey, "Your sister was here, and she's married."

Daysey replied, "She is not."

"Yes she is. I know who she is. She is awful pretty, and her name is Mrs. Beardsley."

Daysey had never heard the name Beardsley. "My sister is pretty," Daysey said, "but she is not married."

The woman's reply was, "She is. She is. You'll see."

Daysey assumed this was just the 'crazy talk' one was always hearing from the patients and to which one paid little attention. However, when Marion next visited, Daysey broached the subject with her. "Marion," Daysey said, "a patient says you're married, but she's crazy of course."

A surprised look crossed Marion's face and then she said, "Yes, it's true, and I was going to tell you when I thought it was the right time. My name is Mrs. Beardsley. That patient must have heard a nurse or doctor talking to me."

Daysey thought no more about this momentous news. Her sister had married an Englishman, Arnold Beardsley, and yet this man, her brother-in-law, was completely unknown to her. This was yet one more significant family development from which she had stayed utterly remote.

During her years in state custody, Daysey had just one real inner satisfaction that no one else knew about. She began to think about what she had learned in the many psychology courses and seminars she had taken at Wellesley and Oxford. The ideas and theories of Freud, Adler, and the other prominent therapists and theorists came flooding back into her brain. She remembered the distinctive signs and symptoms of various neuroses and psychoses, and she could recall in detail their natural histories and sequelae. In the bleak day room, she would look at her companions, observe their actions (or inactions), and then classify their afflictions.

> "That old woman who sits all day, arms folded, rocking herself back and forth, is catatonic."
> "That one ranting all the time is manic."
> "The one who keeps suspiciously glancing around and calling herself 'Josephine' is paranoid."

Daysey's neurons were firing, the memory centers of her brain were returning to life, and all of those facts and fine details were strangely, miraculously, as sharp and distinctive as they once had been, apparently unsullied by her brain's years of inactivity.

Daysey had not switched, in a single instant, as my neighbor, Emily, originally told me, from being insensate to being restored to brilliance, shouting "That's not at all what Freud meant." But, she had begun to reconnect with the world at last, and the connection was coming through her professional knowledge of psychiatric diseases.

Daysey said she never tried to identify and classify her own illness. But she eagerly evaluated those of others.

Still, she often did reflect on why she was being made to live among the insane. She kept returning to the scenario that had first occurred to her in Oxford—that she had committed a heinous criminal act but had not been considered responsible for her actions; thus, she assumed a judge had chosen to place her among the insane rather than among hardened criminals.

What unforgivable act could account for her life-long incarceration?

Her recurring assumption was that she had done something horrible to her friend, Julia, or to Julia's husband during her last troubled days in London. She knew that she had been driven nearly mad from lack of sleep. Had she killed or injured one or both of them on that awful night?

"I had a vague, haunting memory of a sleepless night at their home before I returned to Oxford," she wrote. "I recalled wandering around the bedroom, opening a top bureau drawer, and being intercepted by Julia—or was it simply a purse?—and hearing the words, 'It wasn't there, was it?' What 'it' was had taken the form in my mind of a revolver. Had I really been looking for a revolver? Could I later have found a revolver and shot Julia or her husband or both of them while they were asleep? Might that account for my having to spend my life incarcerated?"

Years after Daysey got well, she continued to stew silently over this, and finally she forced herself to casually say to Marion one day, "Whatever happened to Julia and her husband?"

"Oh," Marion answered, "they're fine, wonderful. I got to know them very well when they were here for a sabbatical year at Princeton."

Daysey felt "untold relief" to finally expunge from her mind the haunting "I am a murderer" hallucination that had troubled her for those long years.

## 1938
## The Comeback

Some two and a half years into her stay at the dreary state hospital, Daysey was sitting one morning in the day room when she glanced up, and there, standing beside her, was a friend from her childhood, Kenneth Appel. She instantly recognized him.

"Kenneth," she said.

"Yes," he said, "I am Kenneth! I've come to visit you often, but this is the first time you've recognized me. "

Kenneth sat down and the two of them began to talk.

"Tell me," he said, "what do you think happened to you in Oxford?"

"I don't know," Daysey said, "I suppose I had a nervous breakdown."

"Oh, no," Kenneth said, "you had a true, organic sickness."

This was a complete revelation to Daysey. Was it possible that she was not crazy or had not, in fact, committed murder? She had no idea until this moment that she had actually been gravely ill.

For Kenneth too, the conversation that day was staggering and transformational. During those seven years when Daysey was in his hospital in Philadelphia, she had never once recognized him. But here she was not only acknowledging his presence without prompting but also sounding like a completely reasonable person. Maybe the time had come to move her back to Philadelphia, where the therapeutic environment at his hospital could support her and perhaps even help her take some steps toward recovery. Maybe she was not, after all, hopelessly and irreversibly insane.

Kenneth quickly contacted Marion, who agreed with his suggestion that Daysey return to Philadelphia. The arrangements were soon set, and shortly thereafter the day came when the doors of the inhumane state hospital closed forever behind her.

Daysey had no memory of the car ride back to Philadelphia. But she did recall a long and protracted delay in the hospital parking lot.

Marion had decided that Daysey should sign her own re-committal papers. So, when they pulled up outside the hospital, Marion put a sheet of paper before Daysey and said softly, "Sign your name to this."

"You know I can't write," Daysey said.

"Yes you can. Take the pen and sign your name," Marion said.

Daysey refused again and again.

The sisters' parley continued for some time, Daysey truly believing that she could no longer write. Twilight came on. Daysey remained stubborn and recalcitrant. She supposed that sheer weariness finally conquered her there in the car, as Marion patiently waited. Finally, Daysey scrawled some kind of signature on the appropriate line, and they walked into the hospital. Daysey mused in her memoir that she would love to see what that scrawl looked like.

Daysey felt no particular emotion at being back in the Pennsylvania Hospital, although she did appreciate having a room of her own, a decent bed with actual linens, and her own clothing. No more hideous state dresses and ill-fitting shoes. No more raucous dining room meals and communal showers. The camel hair coat was now all hers.

The doctors and nurses in Philadelphia continued to work with and hover around her, and she continued to resent their ministrations. She remained intentionally mute, not just when staff members tried to talk to her, but also when groups of young women and men "with their writing pads and pens on the ready" came to interact with her and the other patients. She realized that these were students on some psychology field trip from somewhere.

"Oh, yes," Daysey said, "I knew who they were. In my student days, I had been one of the ones who made such trips. Well, they would get no data from me to discuss in their classroom! I resisted all of their inquiries."

Those students. How she envied their freedom. Oh, to simply open that door and go out anywhere on her own—that was her strongest wish, a wish she knew had no chance of fulfillment.

Kenneth Appel was now taking full charge of Daysey. He had started as a medical resident at the Pennsylvania Hospital but was rising steadily in the psychiatry department; eventually he became its chairman. In the late 1920s, he had taken time out to go to Paris to study neurology and to undergo psychoanalysis with Otto Rank, who was also analyzing Henry Miller and Anais Nin around that time.

Appel was both an accomplished clinician and an outspoken advocate for the mentally ill. He opened the first outpatient clinic for psychiatric patients in the 1930s at the Pennsylvania Hospital, fought for decades for increased federal funding for mental health research, and, much later, was instrumental in getting the U.S. Congress to pass the Mental Health Act of 1963, which President Kennedy signed into law just weeks before he was shot. When Appel died in 1979, a colleague eulogized him as "the conscience of professional psychiatry," a man known for "his probity and stature, good cheer, patience and gentle persistence." Appel had once written, "You cannot see eye to eye with a person you look down upon. We need to be looking eye to eye in psychiatry."

Appel knew from Daysey's Oxford medical records that her protracted illness had begun with encephalitis lethargica, but for reasons of his own he never told her that. By the time Daysey came under his care, he had seen and worked with many patients with the disease.

In a book that he co-authored with a colleague, Appel wrote the following about encephalitis lethargica:

"The disease is an infection and not merely a degeneration ... A patient is often thought to have a severe cold or grippe, being sick in bed with a rather high fever, headache, and marked malaise. ... It is probable that there are multiple etiologies for encephalitis."

"The pathology ... is marked in the parts of the brain called the basal ganglia and mid-brain. This deeper area of the brain ... (affects) muscle tone, the control of automatic action, and especially the expression of instinctive and emotional reactions. ... the illness in the great majority of these patients has not been fatal."

Appel's experience had been that most patients (80-95%) did not die, but most of the survivors (60%) never fully recovered either.

The presenting symptoms for Appel's patients were headache and a feeling of malaise, followed by fever, somnolence, aberrations in the eye muscles, and various paralyses. Then, facial and muscle twitching began, the patients became rigid, and experienced convulsions. The acute phase typically lasted for three week but might go on much longer. During that period, his patients showed no distinctive mental aberrations. Most survivors, though, developed long-lasting neurological complications, personality changes that were termed "bad behavior," hyperactivity, reversed sleep rhythms, and delirium.

"So long as it can be said, 'we have not

seen complete recovery from the behavior disorder,'" wrote Appel and his co-author, "one realizes the importance of trying to develop a technique for helping this group in our communities." That was why he had established a school for affected children and that was also why Kenneth did not expect Daysey to ever fully recover. Still, he never gave up on his efforts to find treatments for her and for his other patients.

At one point during Daysey's second stay in Philadelphia, Kenneth suggested to Marion that they might try electroshock therapy. The salutary effects of this new therapy had been documented for patients in deep depressions, but Kenneth couldn't guarantee anything for someone in Daysey's situation. Still, as he put it, "everything else known to science has been tried on her to no avail. Perhaps shock therapy will activate some of her healthy brain cells and reintegrate them."

He was concerned, though, about the crudeness of the technology. Some people who received electric shocks suffered from broken bones when the current was administered. Was it worth trying? It was up to Marion to give permission or withhold it.

Marion decided that she could not subject Daysey to the risks.

Years later, when Daysey had fully recovered, she toured a private mental hospital with a college friend who had become a psychiatrist. They walked through a sitting room where several patients who had undergone shock treatments that day were sitting around, quietly playing a card game.

As they drew close to the card table, Daysey noticed that a number of the players were holding their cards upside down, apparently unfazed by the reversal of the pictures.

"Their confusion is only temporary," her hostess had said. "They currently lack perception and memory, but tomorrow they will not be confused."

Daysey felt so thankful, after seeing those patients, that Marion had vetoed the treatment for her, although she realized that, of course, she could never know what the results might have been.

Daysey characterized her routine at Pennsylvania Hospital as unvarying—long hours in the day room, daily walks with attendants on the hospital grounds, the familiar and often-repeated injections.

At some point, she started to enjoy her sister's visits, especially when Marion took her out for a drive. Those small tastes of freedom allowed her to see how the world had changed, "the suburban towns, the pretty houses, the manicured lawns."

Still, Daysey remembered thinking as they drove, "How foolish for this car to be moving straight ahead toward where we will drop off into space." She never said this out loud to Marion, she never actually felt fearful, and they always returned safely to the hospital. But she sensed that a catastrophe was waiting for them; probably it would occur the next time they went out for a drive. She never figured out whether this anxiety was based on lingering optical illusions or was a residue of the compulsion she had felt at the Warneford that her life must end. She only knew that space stopped just ahead of them, and drop off the edge of the world they must.

Marion kept seeing improvements in Daysey. She would report to Kenneth Appel that Daysey was speaking freely and lucidly, often for an hour at a time. But Kenneth was not seeing these advances, and he kept discouraging Marion from having hope that Daysey was going to fully recover. He would say, "You don't see your sister when you have gone. The mask falls again and she remains uncommunicative. That mask is characteristic of post-encephalitic patients, and she will never lose it."

In an oral history recorded in 1978, Kenneth Appel reflected on his experience treating Daysey, whom he characterized as "a hopeless patient."

"A case that taught me a tremendous amount in psychiatry was that of a patient who had graduated from Wellesley, then went on to Oxford, England, and got some sort of kidney infection. She was hospitalized in Oxford with delusions and hallucinations, and she was then brought over to this country. When she came here, her Wellesley classmates raised $25,000 to try to help her with her treatment. Her father had been a general practitioner in a small town near Lancaster, and I knew her and I knew him and so they turned to me." ...

"By accident, by serendipity, I would say, a young girl, maybe thirty years old, came by my office one day and said that, although she had been successful in business, she wanted to do social work. Could I help her in any way to get some training? I hired her for a sum of $30 a week to care for this very sick girl who was having delusions, hallucinations, was incontinent, and was paranoid. ... I told her that I wanted her to sit by the side of the bed of this sick girl for one hour a day. ... I said, 'I don't care what you do, whether you knit, you talk of Shakespeare, read the Bible, but just sit by the side of her bed, even if you don't talk, hear what she talks about, what she says. Do that an hour a day, six days a week.'"

"Well, that was the beginning of the recovery of this patient. ... It wasn't anything didactic, it wasn't anything theoretical, it was just a sort of social relationship, a kindly relationship, someone being in touch with her, on whom she counted every day. ... She made a complete recovery after years of schizophrenic symptoms."

"Well, that case probably taught me more than any other bit of experience I ever had, because it taught me about the social relationship of one human being to another in helping people recover."

"This patient ... recovered completely and for years lived a useful life. I haven't heard from her for a number of years now, but I used to know that things were going along all right. In my work with this patient, I didn't know whether it would work or not; she had had insulin and two years of the best medical treatment at Oxford. So I couldn't think of anything else, any other medication."

145

"... when you were up against a delusional patient, a schizophrenic patient, talking about insights, about the patient coming to some understanding of his or her condition, was out of the question. But there was something more fundamental that one could advise and I thought this relationship with someone sitting by the bed would be helpful."

Daysey said nothing of daily conversations with this "hired" sitter. It was Marion she credited with steadfastly being at her side and having the stamina and optimism and creativity that eventually drew her back into life. And Daysey mentioned nothing about interactions with Kenneth at all, except for his cameo appearance at the state hospital when he pronounced her illness "organic."

In fact, Daysey mentioned only one positive encounter with a person at the Pennsylvania Hospital, besides Marion, during all those years in Philadelphia. A nurse who had somehow made a favorable impression on her had said, "You once taught at Tenacre, didn't you? I graduated from a school much like that."

Instead of refusing to respond as usual, Daysey said, "Yes, I did teach there."

"Well," the nurse said, "I predict that someday you'll be back teaching at a place like that again."

Daysey did not react to or dwell on this prophecy at the time, but she said she never forgot it.

## 1940

## Sprung

Marion continued to have hope that Daysey would recover. She nourished the dream of taking Daysey out of the hospital and giving her more autonomy and physical freedom in a private home. Kenneth Appel remained pessimistic.

"You see improvement when you are with her," he said to Marion, "but, for someone with damaged brain areas, such improvements are only momentary. There can be no lasting change. You must accept the need for institutional care for Daysey as long as she lives."

But, finally, in the spring of 1940, Marion announced to Kenneth that she had arranged with the owner of a small farm in southern New Jersey to take Daysey as a boarder. Kenneth continued to object.

"I am afraid if you take her away from the institutional routine she will suffer a nervous breakdown," he said.

But then he gave in.

"After all," he said, "you are her guardian, and you are assuming the risk. If you will agree that I can go down to the farm once a week to examine her, I'll give my consent to your experiment, although I don't really sanction it."

Thus came Daysey's release.

**1940**
**Progress**

Daysey was delighted with her new life. The "modest garden farm" was owned by a young couple, "a good-natured farmer and his French-American wife." They had agreed to look after Daysey, bring meal trays to her room, get her out in the fresh air every day, and take her in the car whenever they went shopping in the small village several miles away.

Fourteen years of institutional life had come to an end.

That Daysey still needed supervision, though, became apparent the first night she was at the farm. Her hostess, Marie, brought dinner to Daysey's room, and there, along with several small plates of food, was a full pack of cigarettes lying in the upper left corner of the tray.

"In my remote past," Daysey said, "I knew I had enjoyed smoking, but of course cigarettes were generally taboo for institutionalized patients. In Pennsylvania Hospital, we were allowed one cigarette after dinner, and smoking always took place in the presence of a nurse, who lighted the cigarette and sat by the patient's side until the last puff. Some of the patients ingeniously stuck a pin into their one precious cigarette, so they could draw on it until it was completely gone."

"My sister had told Marie that she could put a cigarette on my dinner tray every night. But on that first evening, I found a whole, enticing, fresh pack of cigarettes, the first unopened pack I had seen in fourteen years! Eagerly I opened the pack. I do not remember whether I ate any food or not, but I shall never forget the thrill of puffing on one cigarette after another without a pause, chain-smoking until I had smoked all twenty cigarettes down to the last stub! Nor shall I forget the dizziness that followed. But what fun it had been. Nor will I ever forget the shocked look on Marie's face when she came in before bedtime to pick up my tray. I am sure that she expected me to drop dead or at least collapse in a dead faint. Nothing dire happened; the dizziness passed. Marie, conscience stricken, made a 'confession' to my sister and, after that, two cigarettes only appeared on my tray each night."

Marie's two daughters were  sixteen and

twelve. Daysey had always been a fine athlete, and she began to play soft ball with the girls and their friends in the afternoons. The older girl was in secretarial school in town; the younger one had entered high school the previous autumn.

The younger girl kept complaining about how difficult her first-year Latin homework was. Daysey offered to take a look at the Latin assignments.

"I glanced through the pages of her textbook," Daysey recalled, "and it all seemed easy and familiar, even though I had not seen a Latin text in some 15 years. I remembered all of the conjugations and declensions. The translations were simple. I offered to help with her Latin assignments, and she accepted. At long last I was doing something interesting, and it gave me such a thrill and such delight. I kept thinking to myself, 'Little do all of those nurses, doctors, and attendants know what I know and what I can do.' Finally, pride and a sense of accomplishment had awakened in me."

Daysey spent a pleasant two years on the New Jersey farm. She wandered around the property as the farmer fed and tended the pigs and chickens; she watched the fall butchering of the pigs and the curing of the hams; she walked along the pleasant little brook that meandered its way along the edge of the meadow; she picked violets and played tag and baseball and other games with the girls and their friends.

Indoors, with her eyes functioning well again, she spent hours "working hundreds of crossword puzzles and reading scores of books" that Marie chose for her each week from the town's public library. Dostoevsky was new to her and, for a while, her favorite.

Marion visited regularly and, on one visit, brought her a handsome, rose-colored, wool sweater that a family friend had knitted for Daysey.

"You should write her a thank-you note," Marion said.

"I can't write," Daysey said.

Marion suggested that it was impolite for Daysey not to acknowledge the gift; she knew that Daysey was doing puzzles and actually could write if she chose to. The sweater was beautiful, but Daysey was stubborn: if she had to write a note in order to keep it then Marion should just take the sweater back. Daysey didn't remember ever yielding on the point, but she did remember wearing the rose sweater for many years.

In the 1940's, there was no such thing as a half-way house. But that New Jersey farm served, for Daysey, as such a place, providing a transitional, safe, and liberating home for her. Her life there was simple, and she was happy. No one made demands on her, and she had no responsibilities.

"I felt no sense of obligation to anybody," Daysey said. "I was not motivated to do anything except enjoy momentary amusements. I had no desire to prove myself in any way, except in the Latin tutoring, which was a constant pleasure."

Kenneth Appel had held to his promise to check on Daysey at the farm, but, after several visits, he reported to Marion that there seemed to be no point in his continuing: she was doing fine, she had made a successful adjustment to the unregimented life, and his fears that she would have a nervous breakdown had vanished.

The entry of the United States into World War II brought Daysey's pleasant rural existence to an end.

The farm was just too far from Manhattan for Marion and Ella (who had sold her house in Strasburg after George died and had moved to Manhattan) to visit Daysey easily. It was time for Daysey to move to New York. Marion packed Daysey up and took her into the city, where she installed her in Ella's apartment (not her own, as my neighbor, Emily, had said).

Daysey's stay in Ella's apartment was a complete disaster.

"I lived there during the winter months," Daysey said, "and refused to go outside. But I could never be left alone. When my mother went out on errands, she had to hire a sitter for me."

"I remember vividly those first battles I fought when my mother tried to induce me to go with her to my sister's apartment, which was just three blocks away. I resisted, even to the point of tears. When she would finally succeed in getting me downstairs and out in front of the apartment, I would refuse to cross the street. I had severe agoraphobia, and it persisted for some time."

"My mother and my sister struggled throughout that winter, and all the while they kept searching for another caretaker — other than a hospital — to relieve them of trying to rehabilitate me themselves."

"I so disliked living in Manhattan that I remember tearfully telling my mother and sister that, much as I hated hospitals, I would rather go back to a hospital than stay in noisy New York. But it was difficult in those war years to find a suitable home for me nearby that they could afford."

Finally, early in the spring of 1942, Marion moved Daysey to Connecticut, where a retired, registered nurse had bought a summer inn that she had turned into a small nursing home. The house accommodated six patients.

Daysey was enchanted with her new home from the moment she first saw it—broad lawns, imposing trees, wide porches. She described herself as the "white-haired child" at the inn, the youngest and most active of the patients, and she adored her life there.

"I only saw two of the other patients," Daysey wrote, "and both of them were lovely. We took soothing rides daily in the countryside and would stop to gather wild flowers. Rather, we stopped, but the nurse did all of the flower gathering. She never urged me to get out of the car, and I never had any desire to do so. Agoraphobia was still menacing me, though back at the inn I roamed at will over those gracious lawns."

Life had once again become deliriously pleasant for Daysey. No discipline, no doctors, no cacophonous city noises. Daysey eagerly helped her hostess plant and weed a victory garden. She had always loved being outside, and the serene, natural setting and beautiful, leisurely rides in the countryside aroused a poetic side in her that had long been dormant.

"I wrote reams of verse that summer," she said. "Today, if I were to sit down and try to write a nature poem, it would be hopeless. But that summer, the outpouring was natural."

One of the old ladies would sit with Daysey on the porch and listen "as I read her my masterpieces. I have a few remnants of my outburst of writing from that summer. Some are quite sensitive; the rest are bland, but harmless."

So, an idyllic summer passed, and Daysey felt utterly grief stricken when Marion appeared one day in the autumn and announced that her stay there was over. Marion had not visited Daysey all summer, as her design work had taken her to the midwest. She told Daysey she had considered this "pleasure house" only a temporary arrangement all along and that she had always planned a change. She had found another nice little home back in New Jersey for her, and she packed Daysey up and off they went again, much to Daysey's chagrin.

The ride to the train station took just a few minutes.

"I had not been near a railroad in years," Daysey said, "and I was terror-stricken by the noise of the big, puffing engine as it bore down on us as we waited on the platform. But somehow we accomplished the journey."

"When we arrived in Trenton, New Jersey, a brisk little business-like woman met us at the station and took us by car to my future home," Daysey said. "I took an immediate dislike to this woman and the bossiness she exuded. Clearly, she was a nurse." She was nothing like the indulgent keeper of the lovely inn where Daysey had been pampered all summer.

But when they arrived in the quiet little town of Crosswicks at the nurse's plain home, Daysey experienced a sliver of a positive reaction.

"I immediately liked the lovely old attractive mahogany furniture," Daysey wrote, but then she went on, "but I was never going to like my guardian. I chafed under the discipline of our daily morning walks. Etta Brown, was, as I had suspected, a nurse, an Englishwoman who wore 'sensible' brown oxfords and walked briskly. The New Jersey countryside was flat and uninteresting. Etta imposed regulations: I had to stay in bed for breakfast; I had to take a morning shower; I had to go with her on a boring walk. After that, though, I was free to read, write verse, work puzzles, and even smoke in moderation."

"One morning during the first week of my stay at Etta's house, she called out to me as she carried my tray up the steps, 'Here comes the principal.' She knew that I had been a teacher, and she thought that she was injecting a bit of humor into the morning routine."

"'Yes,' I answered, 'the principle boss.'"

"I was hostile and humorless, and it was not until some years later, when Etta and I met again and she reminded me of this incident, that both of us were able to laugh about it."

Still, that November marked the start of five months of real progress for Daysey. She conceded that Etta's regulations had been, in fact, "few and reasonable." She began to meet Etta's friends — affable, pleasant women close to her own age who, like Etta, had lived in Crosswicks most of their adult lives.

Life soon took on new interest for Daysey. People would drop in almost daily, and Daysey and Etta would call on their friends, stay for lunch or dinner, play cards, and chat. The days had a routine, but it was a leisurely one. Daysey doubted that any of her new friends knew or cared what sort of illness she was recovering from. She was simply an almost well, former patient who had come to live in their town until she had fully recuperated. Etta's friends offered Daysey authentic friendship and genuine hospitality, and Daysey soon stopped resenting her hostess's style.

"I had become part of a mainstream of normal people, narrow as the stream was," Daysey wrote.

Even so, that winter (1942-1943), Daysey's behavior was still not what one would characterize as 'normal.'

"A week before Christmas," Daysey wrote, to illustrate the point, "I went to Trenton with Etta and one of our nice friends to do some shopping. We parked on the street in front of the department store. They got out of the car and began to help me out of the back seat. 'No, I'll stay here,' I said. 'Take your time in the store. I don't want to get out.'"

"But you need to buy presents for your mother and sister," Etta said.

"Here is my money; you choose the gifts for me," I said. "I never get out of a car."

The truth was that, in all of her rides into the Connecticut countryside and into the village near the New Jersey farm, Daysey had, in fact, never gotten out of a car away from home. She was certain that she was not going to risk getting out of the car in Trenton that day.

But Etta and her friend persisted.

"Of course you are coming into the store with us. We'll each take one of your arms. Nothing can harm you."

To their continued insistence, Daysey answered, "I will faint right here if you make me get out of this car."

Somehow, the two women prevailed and got Daysey out of the car and into the store. Daysey did not faint, and, from that moment on, she was no longer a victim of agoraphobia.

Daysey cited a second example of how unnatural her social behavior still was that winter. A few days after the shopping trip, Etta brought several packages to Daysey's room and piled them on a chair. Then, on Christmas morning, Etta suggested that Daysey open the gifts from her mother and sister. No, Daysey didn't care to. Etta did not press the matter, but during the day she repeated the suggestion several times, and Daysey's reply was always "no."

That evening, friends came to visit. One suggested that Daysey open her gifts. Once again Daysey said no.

"How disappointed your mother would be to think you didn't want to see your gifts on Christmas Day," her friend said, and something about the way she had put it resonated with

Daysey, who then willingly opened her packages.

That winter and into the spring, Etta drove Daysey into Trenton once a week for appointments with a dentist who was rebuilding Daysey's mouth, restoring her teeth, and undoing the wanton abuse to her mouth that had been inflicted by the state hospital's dental clinic. The project took months, but in the end Daysey had a full set of functional teeth again.

## 1943
### 'Normal'

How to account for the dramatic change in March, 1943, Daysey wrote, when, one day, she woke up feeling 'normal?' It was that simple: she was the old Daysey again.

"When I reflect on the transition today," Daysey said, "I am amazed at the speed of my coming back."

Her first thought was to move away from Etta's protective care and get a job. She began to put pressure on Etta, Marion, and her mother to let her move out on her own. She was doing more and more things by herself at that point—taking her daily walks by herself, reading, managing her days. What was the value of continuing with this supervision?

Etta, of course, was cautious.

"A person who has been ill for seventeen years can't suddenly just walk out into the world and withstand the strain of work," Etta argued.

163

"But you know I am really well," Daysey replied.

"You are so well that no hospital would take you," Etta said, "but going out on your own is something else. Maybe by the fall you will be ready."

Throughout that spring, Daysey's physical energy kept growing. She wanted to "do something." She looked around and suggested to the next door neighbors that she mow their lawn. The neighbors agreed and paid her fifty cents. That was the first money she had earned in seventeen years, and what a thrill it gave her. And that just whetted her appetite for more work.

One evening, Daysey and Etta were having dinner at the farm of some friends. The table conversation turned to the farmer's difficulty finding workers to harvest the strawberry crop, which was almost ripe. The farmer had said, "Who would want to go out in the field and pick for five cents a box?"

"I would!" Daysey said.

Etta once again strenuously objected.

"You can't be out in the hot sun for hours on end, stooping to pick strawberries."

"Just try me," Daysey said. "I'll call Marion and get her permission."

And so, while the crop lasted, Daysey "knelt in the sandy field chatting with the negro pickers, carefully filling those forty-cent boxes, for which we laborers were paid five cents a box. The first day I was greeted with, 'Lady, if you never done no pickin' before, what a back you'll have tomorrow.'"

Both Marion and Etta felt that Daysey should not spend eight hours a day in the sand and sun, but they agreed to a compromise. About one o'clock every day, Etta would return to the field to collect Daysey and take her home for her bath and lunch. Daysey never left the field before collecting the forty or fifty cents that she had earned during the morning hours.

"I was so enthusiastic about this work that I extracted a promise from the farmer to hire me for bean picking when that crop was ready," Daysey said.

"My enthusiasm for working increased with this trial, but where could I get a real job? What could I actually do? I knew that teaching again was absolutely out of the question: who would hire someone with a seventeen-year record of incarceration in a psychiatric hospital?"

Daysey began reading the want ads in the Philadelphia papers. The war was still raging, and most of the listings for women were for typists and chambermaids.

"I had never learned to type and bed-making had never been my forté," Daysey said. "But one day my eye fell on a 'Help Wanted' ad for educated women, especially women who were free to travel. Ah! This might be an 'open sesame' for me. With my sister's permission, but still facing Etta's vigorous objections, I traveled up to Philadelphia for a job interview."

"A kindly grey-haired woman in charge of personnel explained that the job was selling a set of children's educational books door to door. The task for the salesperson was to explain the series in detail to prospective buying parents. As I leafed through the volumes, I saw that the books were well written, and I knew I was definitely interested."

"As the interviewer read my resumé, she was struck, of course, by my seventeen-year gap in employment."

"'You were rising in your profession as a teacher until 1926. Why the break until now?' she asked."

"'I've been in the hospital,' I said."

"'But surely not for seventeen years,' she said."

"'Yes, unfortunately,' I replied."

"'But nobody stays ill for seventeen years!' the interviewer gasped."

As the conversation went on, Daysey explained what had happened to her and then learned that her interviewer was a Christian Scientist who felt that restoring Daysey into the workforce was a "moral necessity."

They agreed that Daysey would take a week to consider with her family whether a door-to-door selling job was right for her.

Daysey left the interview and, instead of returning to Crosswicks, traveled on into New York, where she spent the week with Marion and their mother, discussing the pros and cons of the selling job. She also combed the New York want ads for other opportunities. In the New York papers, too, she saw the posting for the 'unusual opportunity for mature educated women.'

Inspired by her success in Philadelphia, Daysey applied for two jobs in New York, one at a door-to-door selling company and one at a Manhattan publishing house.

The publisher's ad appeared to be for menial work—clipping, pasting—but Daysey was eager to pursue any job opportunity that the company might offer. The interviewer at the publishing company was a young and confident woman, who sat legs crossed, smoking leisurely at her desk. After reading Daysey's resumé, she looked up and casually asked, "What happened in that seventeen-year gap in your job record? Were you married and divorced, and now want to work again?"

"No," Daysey said, "I was hospitalized."

"What in the world ailed you all that time?" asked the interviewer. "No one can be in a hospital for seventeen years and then suddenly be cured."

"Well, I am cured," Daysey said. "You see me. Here I am, I'm well, and I want to work."

"I'm sorry," the young woman said curtly. "We wouldn't think of taking such a chance."

Daysey was hurt, but she wasn't exactly surprised. She had suspected that certain doors might be slammed in her face when her long illness came to light. Now she had seen the actual face of a person who was such a door slammer.

But the next day, to her relief, she was interviewed for the door-to-door selling job and was offered a position much like the one that she had been offered in Philadelphia. The salary in New York was $5 more per week. No questions had come up about the seventeen-year gap in her work record. And the New York firm was offering an additional inducement—the chance to advance to a supervisor's job in two years if she did well pounding the streets and selling. By working for the New York company, she could live closer to Marion and Ella.

Daysey returned to New Jersey, packed up her belongings, and said farewell to Etta. She was going out on her own.

## 1943
## Working

For ten days, Daysey attended a "psychology of selling" course at the New York company's corporate headquarters. The selling strategy was straightforward, even easy, and she quickly memorized her sales pitch. Then, armed with a set of demonstration books, she set off for Torrington, Connecticut, an industrial city, which was to be her sales territory.

She took a room in the home of "a merry old lady I liked very much. My landlady, the two other boarders—both public school teachers—and I formed a most congenial household."

Daysey worked hard that summer, but she didn't find the work difficult. And the small pay check she received at the end of each week not only covered her room and board but gave her tremendous satisfaction.

"Every day, I rode off on my bicycle to entice buyers, often to the shouts of children playing in the streets," Daysey recalled. "'Hi, grandmother,' the children yelled. My grey hair, crowning a bicycle, obviously intrigued them."

In the door-to-door business, agents were expected to make an average of eight calls a day. No materials were sent out ahead. The process was called "cold selling." Some days, Daysey was successful; some days she returned home "bone weary with not a single sale." And although the dry stretches sometimes went on for days at a time, she still felt thrilled to be on her own and engaged in interesting work. She was finally and fully back in the real world, and she was functioning fine among the living.

Daysey found the young mothers to whom she gave her sales pitch to be ready listeners, whether they said they could afford the books or not. But she felt tremendous sympathy whenever a woman looked longingly at the sample display and then said, "My son has to have his tonsils out. That's going to take all of the money we can spare." She knew she could never, in good conscience, put pressure on someone to make a purchase, and that suggested to her that she really was not meant to be a cut-throat saleswoman. A woman's need to use her limited supply of money for a tonsillectomy or to replace a broken furnace always cooled Daysey's selling ardor. One happy day, however, lingered warmly in her memory—the day that she made three sales and $45.00 in commissions.

Often, on hot days, as Daysey cycled around Torrington, kind women would offer her a glass of iced tea or ginger ale. She kept noticing how neatly cut the ice was in the glasses.

"What sharp knives these households must have," Daysey recalled thinking, "in order to get such regular pieces of ice. Back in the 1920's, when I last knew iced drinks, we had always gone to the ice box with the faithful ice pick. The result was irregular chips and chunks--no neat little cubes. I happened to mention this to Marion one day; she was very amused and showed me the little trays from her freezer that were in everybody's refrigerators in the 1940's." (This story is obviously the one that my neighbor, Emily, had moved to a different location—a restaurant—and different time—when Marion was first experimenting with taking Daysey out of the Pennsylvania hospital.)

Daysey's days in Torrington were busy, but her evenings were free. She spent hours each night systematically reading old copies of the New York Times in the Torrington town library (not the New York Public Library or the Library of Congress, as her friends had said), informing herself about American involvement in the

Second World War, of whose beginnings she had been completely unaware.

She was eager to learn about the Nazis — a word that was unfamiliar to her — about Pearl Harbor, and about other aspects of the war. "I still knew nothing about the war," Daysey wrote. "Hitler, for example, remained for me the disruptive patient at the state hospital whom the newsboy always shouted about."

Before she had gotten sick, Daysey's peers were going off to fight in the First World War, and several of her friends had never returned. Now it was the young sons of her peers who were going overseas to fight this new and terrible war.

She quickly became a fervent admirer of Franklin and Eleanor Roosevelt and Winston Churchill. She devoured stories of the pilots, Charles Lindbergh and Amelia Earhart, whose names were new to her. She loved reading about the British king who had abdicated his throne in 1936 for 'the woman he loved,' and she was excited when she connected the dots between him and the charming Prince of Wales who had attended Lady Astor's spring ball in Oxford when she, too, had been there. (Lady Astor always invited the American and other foreign students who were studying at Oxford to her ball.) She remembered how the prince had been socially lionized during his visits to North America in the early 1900s.

It was some time before Daysey had any real understanding of the Great Depression. By the time she recovered, "the boom times of war production" were at hand, and the Depression rarely came up in conversations. But, from bits and pieces, she began to understand how terribly people had struggled in those years.

"Once, when I inquired about an old friend, my mother said, 'Theirs was one of the tragedies of the Depression. In the early days of that sad time, the father of the family suddenly lost not only all of his family's fortune but was also responsible for having made bad stock investments for some of his clients. When the crash came, he could not take the disgrace. He added to the grim calamity by going upstairs in that lovely home of theirs and putting a revolver to his head.'"

That family was the most affluent one Daysey had known growing up. She often spent time playing at their home and enjoying "many a happy swim in their lovely landscaped pond." Daysey had last seen those friends in the 1920s.

"Theirs had been such a happy picture," Daysey recalled. "Everyone was fun-loving. The mother was a busy, hospitable woman, the father a prominent lawyer, the two older daughters had gone to Wellesley, the two boys had gone to Princeton, and the younger daughter was still in preparatory school on my last visit. Now they were all hard at work. I was surprised to learn this."

"They have been very brave about adjusting," Ella told Daysey. "The younger children had to give up college immediately and go to work, like everyone else. They now live in a small rented house. Their mother bakes fancy cakes for sale and her daughters deliver them to the houses of customers."

Another time, Daysey asked her mother why Marion was working so hard now that she was married. Her mother's laconic reply was, "Oh, everybody works today."

Shortly after her recovery, Daysey mentioned to an old friend "who had always handled reality with a light touch" that she had missed so much and had so much catching up to do. But her friend said, "Oh, you didn't miss a thing by not being around in the 1930s. It offered nothing for us except having the children's tonsils and appendices out, child after child, and struggling through the Depression."

The world that Daysey returned to in the 1940s was an anxious one. Daysey began to follow the progress of the war. She wished that she could join the women's forces, but this she knew to be an impossible dream. One day, a former pupil looked her up, having heard that she had 'come back.' Daysey recalled that the young woman "looked so impressive in her WAVE officer's uniform. But me, I was lucky to be selling books!"

Daysey's selling job had begun in June, and, by November, she felt that she had exhausted the market in Torrington. The New York office was about to reassign her elsewhere "to plough new ground." It occurred to her that she might find a similar job in Boston, a city that she had loved during her Wellesley days.

The Boston papers did indeed run the now-familiar "educated women, free to travel" want ads. She sent a letter of inquiry to a Boston firm and was given an appointment to meet the personnel manager. She took the train into Boston one Friday morning and had a brief interview. The interviewer was pleased to find an experienced saleswoman, and she offered Daysey a slightly higher commission than she was currently receiving because of her experience. Daysey left the office with a promise

that she would re-contact the interviewer in a
week, after she had arranged her release from
her New York employer.

## 1943
## Sentimental Journey

Those few hours in Boston roused in Daysey a sudden desire to see Wellesley, which was just outside of town. She had loved living in the Wellesley-Boston area all those long years ago. She was curious now to see the town, the college, and the prep school where she had taught before her move to Oxford. She was not interested in looking up her old professors at the college or her teaching colleagues at the Tenacre School; she just wanted to see the lovely trees, the familiar buildings, and the gorgeous grounds where she had spent so many satisfying years.

She had the time. It was just midday. She didn't need to hurry back to Torrington, so she caught a suburban train out to Wellesley instead.

The town had retained its quiet charm and gritty New England character. The peacefulness of the autumn afternoon was intoxicating. As she walked across the campuses and through the town center, happy memories flooded back into her mind. Soon, she was filled with great melancholy and a yearning for what once had been. Such gracious elegance, and so many things looked exactly as they had decades earlier. Had time really stopped here? Daysey was staggered by these thoughts and the depth of her feelings. Suddenly, her disinterest in seeing people connected to her long-lost past simply evaporated.

She remembered that, in her most recent Wellesley alumnae magazine, a classmate had written that she was working as a house director at the Tenacre School. Why not look her up?

She strolled pensively back to Wellesley village and up the familiar street to the beautiful colonial house that, in her day, had been the home of the administrator of Tenacre, Helen Temple Cooke. Perhaps the person who now lived in Miss Cooke's house could direct her to the dormitory where she would find her classmate.

"What nostalgia surfaced in me as I walked up to the handsome doorway that I knew so well," Daysey wrote.

She rang the bell. The door opened and then—what an astonishing coincidence! There stood Lillias MacLane, whom Daysey had known as a dining-room maid at Wellesley

College all those years ago. Nobody could mistake Lillias, who was unusually tall, almost six feet, and who spoke with "that old familiar Scotch burr I knew so well."

Lillias shared Daysey's stupefaction, and, after just a momentary puzzled look, she said, "Why, Miss Day!"

"Yes," Daysey responded, "that's who I am!

They talked for a short while, and then Daysey asked for the address of her classmate.

"Oh, she got married during the summer and is no longer here," Lillias said. "But come in. We have her forwarding address. Let me get it for you."

"As I stepped into that beautiful, high-ceilinged hall," Daysey said, "the memories rushed at me. How many times I had been here to dinners in those days so long gone! What an abyss had swallowed me up so soon after I left this tranquil place!"

Daysey wondered if Miss Cooke were still alive. Lillias would know; she would ask her when she returned. Miss Cooke had been such an exemplary woman, and she had always been so supportive of Daysey's work. Miss Cooke's excellent stewardship of Tenacre and the other Dana Hall schools had garnered her an outstanding reputation as an educator, and she was in fact one of the best-known school administrators in the northeastern United States. Daysey had adored every minute of the six years that she taught under Miss Cooke's supervision.

Daysey sat there, lost in her thoughts of the past. The hall was large, elegant, dimly lit, so still. It seemed not to have changed one bit. She sat quietly, barely moving, hardly turning her head or raising her eyes, just waiting for Lillias to return with the address.

Some minutes passed, and then Daysey noticed a movement on the stairway. A small woman, beautifully and formally dressed, was coming quickly down the steps. Could it be? Oh my. It was Miss Cooke! No one could mistake that sprightly, quick step and forthright manner. Gray-haired, petite, the head of school herself.

"I had no intention of coming out of my secluded corner to make myself known," Daysey wrote. "It was enough satisfaction for me to see Miss Cooke looking so in command, just as she had always been when I was young and one of her teachers."

Daysey made no sound, nor did she move. But Miss Cooke seemed to be fully aware that she was there, and she was walking purposefully toward her. So, Daysey stood up and stepped out of the dark corner, ready to explain that she was awaiting Lillias's return with an address.

Miss Cooke stopped, looked into Daysey's face with her "flashing blue eyes, as bright as I remembered them," and, before Daysey could speak, Miss Cooke softly marveled, "No, it can't be. You can't be Marjorie Day. They said she died."

"Yes, I'm really Marjorie Day," Daysey said. "I'm waiting for Lillias."

"But you! Where did you come from?" Miss Cooke said. "We must talk. But, as you can see," she continued, motioning toward the library that opened off the great hall, "my board of trustees is here now, and they are waiting for me."

Daysey could see the long refectory table where a dozen black-coated men were already in their chairs, and she started to withdraw with "Of course."

"I must talk with you," Miss Cooke continued. "Can you come back tomorrow morning? This meeting will take all evening."

"I'm on my way back to Connecticut," Daysey said. "That's where I work. That's where I live."

"Doing what?"

"Selling books."

"Oh no," Miss Cooke said. "I have to see you. They said you had died. Can't you plan to stay in town over night?"

It was Friday afternoon. Daysey did not work on Saturdays. She could actually stay in Wellesley over night and return in the morning. Miss Cooke's surprise and delight at seeing her were so genuine and her desire to talk to Daysey seemed so heartfelt. Daysey realized that she, too, was at long last eager for a proper reunion.

"I'll go down to the Wellesley Inn and get a room there for the night," Daysey said, "and I'll come to see you tomorrow."

"Very well, at ten, and plan to stay to lunch," Miss Cooke said. And once more she said, "I must talk with you."

How wonderful to feel so welcomed and so prized. And what an amazing development— so unplanned and unexpected. This was not the serendipitous encounter in the middle of Manhattan that my neighbor, Emily, had described. It was, however, a stunning reunion, thrilling for both Daysey and Miss Cooke.

And it proved to be the turning point in Daysey's professional life.

That night at the inn, Daysey ordered a sumptuous meal and luxuriated in her elegant surroundings and her good fortune. She had a new selling job waiting for her in Boston. She would choose a nice place to board in town, and it would be wonderful to have time to explore that city again. She might even be able to travel out to the coast on occasional weekends. And she could visit Wellesley easily from town. She had not found her classmate, but finding Miss Cooke was so much better! This had been a remarkable day.

Promptly at ten the next morning, Daysey walked the few blocks from the Wellesley Inn back to Miss Cooke's home. Miss Cooke was waiting and immediately began firing off questions.

"Where have you been?"

"What was it like?"

"When did you recover?"

Daysey was struck by the insistence of her interrogation. She couldn't understand at first why Miss Cooke was so focused on her long illness and her period of insensibility rather than on her presence in the room and what she was now doing with her life. But, as the morning went on, Daysey learned that Miss Cooke had, at the death of her own sister a few years earlier, developed a keen interest in the occult. Miss Cooke had been attending seances in Boston, where the medium assured her that she would be able to communicate with her dead sister.

"What do you recall?"

"How did you get back?"

The questions went on.

As Daysey watched Miss Cooke's fervor grow, she realized that Miss Cooke was picturing those seventeen years she'd spent in coma and then 'away' as a mystical or magical time, and she knew that she had to bring the conversation back to the realities of her own, agonizing experience in that netherworld.

"It was horrible out there," Daysey said, "just like a jail."

Miss Cooke started then to ask about Daysey's family, but that conversation also quickly turned problematic.

"Unfortunately," Daysey said, "my father died long ago when I was ill, in 1930."

"Oh, no, he didn't die," Miss Cooke said.

"Oh, yes, it is true," Daysey said prosaically, still not grasping the extent of Miss Cooke's belief in the supernatural. "But my mother and my sister are still living."

"My dear, your father did not die," Miss Cooke said again and again.

Daysey felt the need to shift the conversation to something more mundane.

185

"I've been selling books, children's educational books," she said. "I've been going door to door since last June. Yesterday, I was offered a new job doing the same thing for a Boston firm, and I'm planning to move to Boston soon."

"You should not be selling books," Miss Cooke said. "You were a gifted teacher. You should return to teaching."

Daysey, who had long suppressed all hope of ever teaching again, savored the compliment.

And then her world changed.

"I would consider it an honor to reinstate you to teaching," Miss Cooke said. "Do you remember how, when you came to resign your position here because you were going to Oxford, I remonstrated? I told you that your future was here at my schools. I said you and I knew that you were an excellent teacher, that you needed no further degree, and that it was foolish for you to leave."

Daysey did remember those conversations and Miss Cooke's arguments. Her colleagues at the school had told her they felt sure Miss Cooke was preparing to offer her a deanship. But even such a promotion had not been a sufficient enticement to keep Daysey in

Wellesley at the time. She had been young, the world held so many opportunities for her, and the pull of Oxford's neo-realists had been irresistible.

Miss Cooke repeated her suggestion that she reinstate Daysey to teaching, and then she made the offer.

"You can have your old Latin job back at Tenacre immediately after Christmas vacation," she said. "Our current teacher will be leaving. She is to be rejoined by her husband, who was a prisoner of war in Europe, but is due to come home in several weeks on the Gripsholm. Will you come after Christmas and resume your old place?"

Was this just a dream? Was she about to wake up and find herself lying in bed in Torrington in the boarding house, or worse, in some hospital somewhere?

The six years Daysey had worked at the Tenacre School had been such happy ones. Why wouldn't she return? They talked on, and Miss Cooke proposed that Daysey return both to teach Latin full time and also to be the house mother for a dormitory of twenty-five girls who were in their first year at the school. What an offer! Daysey would have a place to live, a salary, living expenses. And, she would be a teacher once again.

After lunch, Miss Cooke took Daysey over to meet the principal of the Tenacre School, under whose direct supervision she would be working. Then, Daysey returned to the train station and made her way back to Connecticut.

What a turn fate had taken. Miss Cooke had plucked Daysey out of the haphazard world that she had been inhabiting for so long and plunked her firmly back down into the world she venerated, the world of education.

**1944**

**Teaching**

Daysey was fifty years old when she once again became a teacher.

She rejoiced, at first, in being back in the classroom. How wonderful it was to immerse herself again in the life of the mind. She had always considered the texts of first-year Latin — the works of Cicero and Virgil — to be the most exacting to teach, and she was eager for the challenge. What joy to be reading Latin again.

But soon after settling in at Tenacre, Daysey encountered problems that she had never before had to contend with. The classroom environment was dramatically altered. Tenacre had been the most progressive school in the 1920s. Here, in the 1940s, the students seemed to lack engagement with their own educations, and the staff acted with such foolish and laissez-faire permissiveness.

Daysey recalled how, one day, in the middle of an explanation of the grammatical

189

uses of the Latin relative pronoun "qui," a "rather dull thirteen-year-old rose from her seat, walked to the window, and announced, 'See the snow, Miss Day. Isn't it pretty!'"

"I didn't ignore her," Daysey said. "I wrote on the blackboard *Pulchra est nix. Videte nivem pulchram* and asked the class to translate." (The snow is pretty; look at the pretty snow.) A good teacher, Daysey knew, could always turn this sort of nonsense into a teaching moment.

Soon she realized that what had made Tenacre so successful in the old days was its leadership, Miss Cooke and the co-principals, Miss Waldo and Miss Lathrop, all of whom had fostered cooperation and camaraderie among the staff. They had been true exemplars for the teachers and steadfast champions of the students. But now, Tenacre was controlled by this new principal who was so authoritarian, so fond of power. Her omnipotent attitude seemed to generate unending friction among the faculty. Three of the teachers were the principal's close personal friends, and they gave her "unwavering support no matter how arbitrary and questionable her pronouncements." Other teachers kept silent, doing their best, as Daysey said, "to preserve their own integrity." But a distressing number of the younger faculty members resented the principal's strong-arm directives and demands, and several actually resigned in midterm that first year.

And what a ridiculous waste it was for the faculty to assemble at 8:30 each morning for a compulsory meeting, at which they were made to sit in silence while the principal read aloud from *The Education of Henry Adams*. Why not suggest that we read it for ourselves, Daysey remembered thinking. We teachers should be spending our time over in the school house answering students' questions, not being read a story like so many kindergartners.

But these were thoughts that Daysey kept to herself. She suspected that the principal was especially irritated to have her on the staff, a "brain-damaged" teacher, thrust on her by Miss Cooke without consultation.

"Although I was reticent at faculty meetings," Daysey said, "this did not go unnoticed by the principal. She surprised me one day by remarking out of the blue, 'Miss Day, you wear a hair shirt around here, don't you?' Still, I let even that remark pass."

"I was observed only once by the principal that first year," Daysey recalled, "on a day when I was trying to make clear to a non-comprehending student some point of Latin syntax. I was asking the student a series of pertinent questions as the principal watched me, listened impassively, but said nothing. Later, she called me to her office."

"Miss Day," she said, "your approach is more like that of a lawyer than a teacher."

"I was bewildered by the critique," Daysey wrote. "My tactic had, in fact, been effective, and I had led that student logically through a sequence of questions to an eventual grasp of the grammar issue that was under discussion."

Toward the end of her first year at Tenacre, Daysey was summoned by the principal. What comment or criticism was coming now? She approached the office expecting a confrontation. But, to her surprise, the principal held in her hand a sheaf of reports that Daysey had written the previous week, in which she had summarized the attitudes and progress—or lack of it—of each of her students.

"These evaluations are excellent," the principal said. "I have never seen such full, understanding comments. I did not dream you had this ability. You really should be in a position where this kind of personality analysis is the focus of your job."

This was the first and only compliment

Daysey ever received from Tenacre's principal. She walked out of the office and headed straight to her dormitory and down into the basement. Tony, the janitor, had found an old wicker chair for her and had placed it next to the furnace so that Daysey could smoke unobserved whenever she needed a moment for relaxation. (The school banned smoking.) Daysey sat there smoking and happy, realizing that she would at least be invited back for a second year of teaching at Tenacre.

## 1944

### Summers

That spring, Daysey was contacted by Marion Niles, a woman she had known in Wellesley in the old days. Marion had long been an activist for women's rights and other important causes—rights of refugees and those who are mentally ill. She was the longtime president of the Massachusetts League of Girls' Clubs and had, for some time, also been the president of the Rockport Lodge, a summer vacation site for working women "sixteen to sixty years of age." She wondered whether Daysey had summer plans and, if not, whether she might be interested in spending the summer working at the Lodge. The current recreation director of the Lodge was going overseas to help entertain the troops, and Marion was looking for someone to replace her.

The job sounded almost tailor made for Daysey, who had always been a sports and nature lover and was a natural leader. The recreation director was responsible for teaching the guests how to play tennis and badminton. She was the organizer of softball games and shuffle board and badminton tournaments. She planned the beach parties, sailing trips, hikes, field trips, and picnics. And she cooked bacon and eggs on the rocks at breakfast time once or twice a week for the forty or fifty guests who were at the Lodge. Marion explained that the "season" lasted ten weeks and that most guests had time and money to spend just one week at the Lodge. But most did return to the Lodge year after year. They were Massachusetts mill and sweat shop workers who greatly valued this respite week.

The position sounded perfect. Daysey was being offered a chance to do all of the things that she loved and even get paid for it. Plus, without a true home anymore, now that both her mother and sister lived in apartments in Manhattan and the Strasburg home belonged to someone else, Daysey would have a place to spend her summers.

She said "yes." That summer, and for the next twelve summers following it, she headed out to Rockport as soon as her spring semester of teaching ended. Her summers among working women—guiding them in sports, drama, relaxation at the sea, hiking, painting and poetry — provided a fascinating counterpoint to Daysey's winters teaching Latin and, later, social science courses to privileged girls and eventually college students.

## Life Idealized

Daysey stayed just two years at the Tenacre School and then moved on. She found great pleasure being reunited with some old friends in Wellesley, many of whom were as surprised as Miss Cooke had been to find that she had actually come back to life. But as she grew increasingly disgruntled with the school's management and its philosophy of education, she decided to accept a job at the Ethel Walker School in Simsbury, Connecticut. There, she was assigned to teach girls who were older than her students at Tenacre, and she lived in faculty housing and had no house-mother responsibilities.

During the next three New England winters, Daysey suffered from three serious attacks of pneumonia. Her doctor was convinced that her long-cocooned lungs simply could not tolerate the harsh northern climate. He recommended that she look for a warmer place to live.

Thus, Daysey moved south, to Washington, D.C., and that move proved to be the real 'open sesame' of her professional life.

Daysey was 54 years old when she arrived in Washington in 1947. Her first teaching job was at the Mount Vernon Seminary, a preparatory school for girls in Georgetown, just outside the District of Columbia. Most students enrolled at the school were the children of power, the daughters of government officials, diplomats, and prominent families.

One benefit of living in the D.C. metropolitan area was that Daysey now could catch up with her field. She enrolled in evening and Saturday graduate courses at American University and at the Washington Psychiatric Institute. Even though much had changed in the social sciences since 1926 and throughout her "suspended" years, she never had trouble taking it all in. She found the course work to be extremely stimulating, and she said it was much easier this time around to get A's on her research papers than it had been when she was young.

After Daysey had taught for two years at the Seminary, Mimi Harper, the young, newly hired dean of the college (and Daysey's eventual best friend, who gave me Daysey's memoir), offered Daysey a position at Mount Vernon's

Junior College, teaching social science courses. There, at last, Daysey began doing exactly what she had always wanted to do.

As Professor of Psychology and Child Development, Daysey taught a range of social science courses: Introduction to Psychology, Child Study, General Psychology, Sociology, Family Relations,. Her classes often included a practicum section. She wrote each syllabus in longhand, because she never really took to typing.

SYLLABUS.    Sociology 101 - 3 hours first
                                     semester
basic text: Green, Arnold Sociology: An Analysis
            of Life in a Modern Society, McGraw
            Hill 3d edition 1960
coverage 1st semester - 1st 17 chapters.
Content: Topics
    1. Physical Environment of the Organism
    2. Society as collective human behavior
    3. The basic social processes
    4. Cultures & their diversity
    5. The Socializing process & its develop-
          universality
       ment of personality
    6. Population & its Distribution
    7. Caste & Class
    8. Mobility
    9. Minority Groups
    10. Ecological distribution (& Community Study
    11. Roles in Division of Labor
    12. Basic Social Institutions with
          special study of American Economic Order
                           "    "   Political  "
    13. Comparative view of the Family in
          cross cultural study.
Very frequent outside reading reports (written
and oral) are required in comparative
texts, special articles, etc. Bi weekly or
weekly written quizzes are used throughout
the semester, & quarterly written tests with an

The years of teaching at Mount Vernon were rich ones, and her students loved her, as did her colleagues. She was scholarly, charismatic, and playful, all at once.

A younger colleague, Jane Highsaw, who taught political science at the college, said that Daysey was "a self-possessed and remarkable person. I would often hear her lecturing through the thin walls of the classroom. She was very forceful, very stimulating, and very energetic. She had high standards and was very demanding. Everyone really liked her, although sometimes a weak student would complain about her."

As to her appearance, Jane said, "Daysey looked disheveled most of the time. She wore the same shabby sweater every day, she usually had a cigarette hanging out of her mouth, and she always smelled of smoke."

"When I first joined the faculty," Jane continued, "I was looking for a tennis partner, and it never occurred to me to ask the oldest member of the faculty. But Daysey did become my tennis partner/opponent, and she was extremely competitive."

In 1976, more than a decade after she had retired from Mount Vernon, the college awarded Daysey an honorary degree, a Doctor of Humane

Letters, citing her for "excellence in teaching" and for being "an inspiring teacher, distinguished educator, wise counselor, and warm friend and exemplar for the college's community of learning and living."

## Rockport

What a contrast Daysey's sporting summers were to her scholar's winters. Each June, July, and August at Rockport, she built campfires on slippery rocks at breakfast time, led guests on character-building hikes through the woods, taught untutored women how to swim and hit a tennis ball, wrote and directed pageants and plays, and turned illiterati into poets. She found her summer work to be "strenuous but delightful."

For many of the guests at the Rockport Lodge, the week at the seashore was their first-ever vacation. They came from mills and factories all over Massachusetts: Fall River, Lawrence, Lowell, Haverhill, Pittsfield, Worcester, New Bedford, and other towns. Many had never before seen the ocean. Many had never eaten a lobster before, or a clam. Many had never before experienced leisure time, laughed so much, or felt such happiness and independence. It is likely that few had ever encountered a woman as talented, jovial, bright, kind, and self-assured as Daysey.

The guests were assigned to rooms in the main, white, clapboard, three-story lodge, which dated from the 1700s, or in the annex, a newer structure. The buildings had space for fifty-two women, and the staff members lived there along with the guests.

Like wealthy girls and teens at elite summer camps, the guests at the Lodge formed tight friendships in their brief time together and declared their allegiances to one another and to the Lodge in simple scrapbooks. They signed

203

their entries with monikers that characterized their recently formed groups: the Five Dare-devils, the Goon Girls, the Four Balls in the Jacks, the Howling Six, the Lazy Three, the Big Three, the Quiet Three, the Little Stinkers, the Gruesome Foursome, the Hula Belles. "We are the pufferettes; alls we do is smoke cigarettes ..." That group met in a small shed, called the Puff Box, that was the designated smoking area, the only one allowed after a fire almost destroyed the Lodge one summer. No men were allowed at Rockport Lodge, nor was alcohol.

Many guests wrote about Daysey in the scrapbooks, thanking "Miss Day" for being "an inspiration," for "working very hard to make everything wonderful," for "tireless efforts to make us all happy," for "making this week complete."

Daysey's assignment was to engage the guests and open their eyes to new experiences. She thought it wise to organize a treasure hunt early each week as a way to "facilitate the getting acquainted period." She posted sign-up sheets for deep sea fishing trips, horseback rides, sails, rowboat excursions, breakfasts on the rocks, badminton and tennis tournaments, field trips, painting classes, and so on. The women could always go swimming at Old Garden Beach or

Good Harbor Beach or at one of the other nearby beaches. They could take short hikes in the woods or walk out to Perrett's Ledge to see the wildflowers and birds and, of course, the ocean.

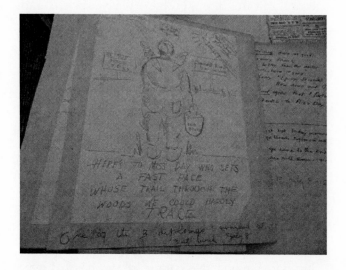

Daysey enlisted Stanley Woodward, a well-known local marine and landscape artist, to teach some painting classes. He was a fixture of Rockport's artist colony, one of the oldest and most famous such colonies in the United States. The women referred to him as "Uncle Stanley." One guest wrote in a scrapbook about her thrill at getting autographs from Uncle Stanley's "friends," who turned out to be Paulette Goddard and Hurd Hatfield, who had just completed the filming of *Diary of a Chambermaid*, and Bette Davis.

A high point each summer was the Rockport town parade on the Fourth of July. The entry from the Lodge was always an extravaganza and always had Daysey's distinctive, creative stamp on it. In 1950, for example, she developed the theme "This is America." First came a huge Liberty Bell, then came a woman dressed as the Statue of Liberty. Next, Hollywood was represented by a Clark Gable look alike, Mae West, Charlie Chaplin and Carmen Miranda. Behind them came Eleanor Roosevelt, followed by a sailor, a farmer, and cowboys. Finally, President Truman made his appearance, proudly pulling Stalin, who lumbered along the parade route, head down, hands tied behind his back, thick rope leash around his neck.

The year after that, Daysey chose a less political theme, "Fairyland." Humpty Dumpty, Prince Charming, the Seven Dwarves, and other cartoon characters showed up in the Lodge's entourage.

Once or twice a week, the guests could sign up for a "breakfast bat" on the rocks. The peppiest guests, the earliest risers, signed on as "Toters"; the rest signed up to be "Eaters." The toters helped carry the equipment and food to the rocks, and there Daysey and two other staff members built a campfire and prepared the morning feast. The women ate bacon, eggs, and toast while watching the sun rise off the coast and warmed their hands and bellies with mugs of hot coffee.

The Rockport area offered a number of unusual tourist attractions that were unrelated to the seashore. A popular field trip took the

207

women to the Paper House, a remarkable building constructed entirely of paper in 1922 by a mechanical engineer. Most of the incredibly ornate furnishings in the house were made of paper too. Another nearby attraction was the Hammond Castle, an actual castle that had been built in the 1920s and housed the owner's Roman, medieval, and Renaissance collections, as well as his many inventions. And just down the road from the Lodge was Dogtown, an abandoned late seventeenth-century village that had played interesting roles in Massachusetts's long history.

Each night and on rainy days as well, the guests would congregate in the big barn, which was just across the road from the Lodge. There, they would square dance or learn some interesting folk dances. They would sit around the piano and sing, play ping pong or shuffleboard or badminton, or simply relax in soft chairs and rockers, read books from the library, and stare contentedly at the jumping flames in the barn's massive fieldstone fireplace.

The Lodge had its own movie projector, and many nights Daysey would show a movie, which at the time was something of a novelty. Some nights the women competed in scrabble, bridge, canasta, and whist tournaments. The

Little Theater upstairs in the barn was home to plays and to the ever-popular Friday night "stunt night" performances. Outfits and props for these spectacles were stashed in the costume closet next to the theater. The guests joyfully accepted the stunt night challenges—act out a mother buying ice cream cones for her six children, reprise a Clark Gable kiss, dance the hula—or dreamed up their own original songs and skits.

Around 10 P.M., everyone collected at the piano for a communal sing. Then, the guests returned to their rooms, often to find that their friends had short sheeted their beds. Lights went out at 11.

"This was the shortest week of the year," one guest wrote in a scrapbook. Others wrote poems (usually doggerel) and simple tributes, and some attested to their best experiences of the week in longer appreciations and drawings. Even those women who did not write easily took time to record something. "May the Kurdesses (courtesies) you give to your guests come back in great measure to each and every one." "I had a wonderful time the girls have been a lot of fun now it time to get to work again I hope I see all of yous next summer if I'm not married by then."

After several summers, Daysey decided

209

to purchase a place of her own in Rockport. She selected a small, pre-Revolutionary building that had originally been an apple shack and later was a shed for goats. She added a loft and a wood-burning stove and moved in. This was the house that she had left in her will to Mimi Harper.

In 2009, I drove out to the coast with my older daughter to visit Mimi in Rockport on a gorgeous summer morning. Mimi and her husband had converted the crude A-frame cottage into an absolutely charming residence. They had added a tiny but proper kitchen, and they had furnished the living area, with its lovely rough-hewn beams, with soft chairs and a couch, bright lamps, paintings, wall hangings, and book shelves. That morning, a vase of cheery, colorful, black-eyed Susans sat on the coffee table.

Mimi had invited the next door neighbors, Enid and David Wise, to lunch so they could tell me about their memories of Daysey. The Wises had moved into their house on Brooks Road next door to Daysey's shack in 1970. Daysey was no longer working at the Lodge by that time, but she was still spending every summer in Rockport. They, like everyone who knew Daysey, smiled the whole time that they spoke about their friend.

"Daysey was so vibrant, ebullient, and

lively," Enid said. "I couldn't imagine that she had that seventeen-year absence. She was just so exciting to be with."

"She was like a hillbilly woman," David said, "but brilliant. All these women who had been at the Lodge would come by to see her. They would sit around her while she sat on her adirondack chair smoking her corncob pipe. She was absolutely charismatic and so jolly. She reminded me of Socrates."

The Wises and Mimi agreed that it was a miracle that Daysey had never burned the cottage down.

"She would stuff long two-by-fours into the stove," Mimi said, "and the ends of them would hang out into the room. I came in one time and the entire length of the wood was burning."

After lunch, we drove over to the shoreline, to look at the place where Daysey had cooked the eggs and bacon for the breakfast bats. The short walk to Flat Rock Point cut through a thick stand of *Rosa rugosa*. Sea gulls were shrieking on the rocks and the view was staggeringly beautiful.

In the distance, we could see the twin lighthouses on Thacher's Island. The Lodge guests often sailed or rowed out there on a sunny afternoon, and that's where centuries of fishermen received their alerts to the nearness and perils of the Massachusetts coast. We were standing on massive granite ledges, the natural outcroppings from Rockport's famous quarries. At the water's edge lay huge boulders, striking reminders that, thousands of years ago, glaciers had covered Rockport, but then receded, leaving their debris behind.

It occurred to me as we stood looking out at the ocean that Daysey had always lived in gorgeous places—Rockport, Wellesley, Strasburg, Oxford. She obviously had an eye for beauty in that prodigious and remarkable brain of hers.

### The Last Thirty Years

Daysey was still thoroughly enjoying her life as a teacher when, in 1964, she reached age seventy, the mandatory retirement age at Mount Vernon College. She had no desire to stop teaching and no interest in becoming a retiree. As she had said on television, she thought she was "owed" the years she had missed, and she was not at all ready to simply fade away into the sunset. Also, she was concerned about money.

She set her sights on Barry Goldwater as she began her last term at Mount Vernon. His daughters were students at the college and, four years earlier, she had done an interesting and lucrative eight-month research project for his office. She was to be on a panel in February with the senator, and she decided to approach him about the possibility of doing some work again for his office.

Several weeks before the panel met, she received a surprising letter from the administrator at Rockport Lodge. They needed her.

213

Could she possibly come back for part or all of the upcoming summer? She had not worked at the Lodge for eight years and that work was a lot more physically demanding than teaching. Still, she was extremely touched by the request and wrote back that, if her plan to get work on Capital Hill did not pan out, "I'll be at the Lodge for the first half of the season and shall be glad you still want the "Old Lady!"

A few weeks later, she wrote another letter to the Lodge's administrator with this update: "I was cordially greeted by my old friend Barry Goldwater on Friday (Fathers Day at our college). He was very surprised when in the very few minutes I had to speak to him I said I would have to go job hunting as I had to retire in June. There was no time for more but at least I put myself on his landscape and hope something will turn up in that direction by fall. (He doesn't know I'm an ardent Democrat, but the work I would do, if it is available, would be research and analysis, not political ballyhoo). Anyway he's aware that I am going to be jobless after this summer."

Goldwater never came back to her with an offer, so that summer, at age seventy, Daysey once again became the Lodge's recreation director.

Just before she headed out to the Lodge that June, Daysey attended her fiftieth class reunion at Wellesley. She was class president at the time, having served in that role since their previous reunion, five years earlier. Her classmates continued to be curious about her sickness and awestruck by her resurrection story, and she loved spending time once again with all of these accomplished women.

The summer of 1964 was a very rainy one, and, in her final report to the Lodge, Daysey listed as the two greatest problems "the weather and the balky film projector." She had once again organized weekly stunt nights (which she characterized as being of the "thought-up-on-Friday" kind), field trips, breakfast bats, sails, swims, and tournaments. She felt that, from the staff perspective, the program had been successful, and she believed that the guests had felt the same, noting "their enjoyment is our constant aim."

That fall, to her great joy, she was invited to be a visiting professor in the sociology department at Northern Illinois University in DeKalb, and that appointment lasted two years. She appreciated the maturity of the students she met there and also enjoyed the opportunity to have men in her classes. And she was teaching a course that she had never before taught: criminology. During the intervening summer, she was asked to teach that same course at Illinois's Rockford College. The college paid her much more than the Lodge could, so, although the Lodge asked her to come back again for the summer of 1965, she decided to decline that offer.

And then the teaching ended for good.

In the final quarter century of her life, Daysey wrote regularly to the Wellesley alumnae magazine, and they published the following entries about what she was doing.

### Age 74: Alumna note: 1967

*I really am not coping too successfully with retirement, as I am still rarin' to go, but nobody here in Washington wants a teacher my age. I'm fed up with joblessness. Maybe I'd better try typing lessons ... but such a bore!*

### Age 75: Alumna note: 1968

*I'm leaving in two days to be a housemother at Cardinal Cushing College in Brookline, Mass. I'm so glad to be employed again.*

### Age 80: Alumna note: 1973

*My big event of last winter was a trip to Mexico, my second since 1970. I do delight in those old Mayan ruins.*

### Age 83: Alumna note: 1976

*This year has been marked by highs and lows. The high was at Mount Vernon's Commencement, when I was given an honorary degree, Doctor of Humane Letters. The lows: I was hospitalized twice with acute sciatic neuritis, and I was disappointed with the rejection of my finished manuscript about my illness and my recovery. But I am not daunted and expect to put it in the hands of a literary agent later in the year when I get back to Washington.*

### Age 84: Alumna note: 1977

*There is not much to record in my uneventful life. I spent the usual leisurely summer in my cottage in Rockport. I took off in September with an old friend on a motor trip to see the autumn foliage in the White Mountains. Back here in Washington I had a brief appearance on TV. The same reporter from NBC who had interviewed me in 1976 after I got my honorary degree called me for this second appearance. I enjoyed seeing what goes on behind the scenes before the lights are turned on full glare. Otherwise, I depend on bridge to break the quietude.*

## Age 85: Alumna note: 1978

*I interrupted my usual inactive Washington life last May to take a nostalgic trip to England and Scotland. It was delightful, though I would have preferred to avoid the dramatic episode of my first day in London, when I was pick-pocketed! My wallet was adroitly lifted from my handbag while I was having a quiet restaurant lunch. But, would you believe it, the very next day I picked up a ten pound English bank note from the bus floor – and insufficient reparation for the loss of the day before, but comforting. Later, while sitting in Heathrow airport before emplaning for home, drinking a cup of coffee and smoking my pipe in that anonymous crowded place, I looked up to see a smiling man across the room pointing his camera directly at me. I can see the snapshot in some small English town paper: "Old white-haired lady smokes pipe in airport!" Right now life is a bit hectic as I am serving jury duty in Washington Superior Court. The actual courtroom experiences are interesting but it is fatiguing to travel the length of the city each morning to be on duty at nine A.M. One of the few luxuries of retirement has been sleeping late in the morning these past twelve years. At age 85, I don't toss off an eight-hour work day as easily as I used to! A friend has called this ailment that afflicts us old people a "youth deficiency." My present task confirms that diagnosis. But let's hang on and look forward to our 65th reunion in 1979.*

## Age 88: Alumna note: 1981

*I live in the nation's capital where news is made every day, but I get my news from my TV. My little house on a tree-lined street, only about 20 minutes from the Capitol, is in an area as quiet as a village street. I live alone, except for the companionship of my 12-year-old cat Josephine, but am not lonely. Josephine and I are most congenial. I sally forth to the National Democratic Club to hear interesting speakers. Travel still lures me – a different place each year. This month I plan to go to Puerto Rico for a short stay. I wish I could report that some editor thought my story about my recovery – The Phoenix – was worth publishing, but no luck there. I am fortunate in having good health, deafness being my only handicap.*

*Living in Washington for 35 years has developed my interest in government and politics. I was always an avid reader and spend hours each day with the news magazines, novels and some history books. When I was an undergraduate, I resolved that when I became an old lady I would reread Paradise Lost and Cicero's De Senectute. But that thirst for erudition no longer survives! Instead, I consume 40 or 50 novels a year. My favorite writer, C.P. Snow, died last year, and I find myself rereading his works and enjoying them a second time. I also find that the Victorian novelists have great appeal. I play bridge each week and am an avid Red Sox fan.*

*I no longer dislike all domestic chores, as I once did. I'm now a willing cook and roast the turkey for the five or six of us who get together each year for Christmas.*

*But I trust the cleaning to a professional.*

Daysey's cleaning woman may have been a "professional," but her carelessness with the front-door key was what kept me from meeting this remarkable woman.

Still, I wonder. Would I have learned more or less about Daysey than I now know had I actually met her?

## 2012
### Lingering Mystery

I have continued to be intrigued by the fact that Daysey never knew that she had encephalitis lethargica. At one point, she wrote to Kenneth Appel to thank him for all that he had done to shepherd her through her protracted illness. She received a note back from him that said, "Don't thank me or any medical person. We were not able to do anything except keep you alive. Doctors do not like to use the word 'miracle,' but in your case, that is the only explanation I can give. What we in medical research don't know about the brain exceeds what we do know. There were a million chances against any recovery for you, but here you are." Kenneth had not chosen to include the words "encephalitis lethargica" in his note, so she never heard these two words from him.

She also never heard these words from Marion or from her mother. And her father, George, never had the chance to say them to her, because he died years before she came back to life.

In 2009, I wrote to Oliver Sacks, whose 1973 book, *Awakenings*, describes hospitalized patients who had contracted encephalitis lethargica during the epidemic of the 1920s. Many of Sacks's patients were later reanimated after drug treatments with L-dopa. Their awakenings were dramatic, but their experiences of wakefulness always seemed to be short lived. I asked Sacks if he had ever seen a patient like Daysey, who recovered completely and permanently.

"I have never seen anything like this in my own practice," he wrote back.

He then continued to reflect: "Awakenings refers to a state—akinetic mutism—in which speech and movement are impossible, but some sort of consciousness is still present. Patients may suddenly come to from such states after being given a drug ... or, in some cases, spontaneously. But it would be rare for such 'awakenings' to be permanent. Several of the *Awakenings* patients had extreme insomnia when they first became ill. Reversal of sleep rhythm was exceedingly common ... I often had to stay up at night, because so many of the patients were awake then, and, like them, I slept in the day. Indeed I saw exactly this pattern in a severely parkinsonian patient I saw this morning—she would look at her TV all night, then be almost unrousable in the daytime till around 5 PM, when she would come to."

Sacks referred me to his colleague, Joel Vilensky, who had recently reviewed the more than nine thousand articles that had been published over the years about encephalitis lethargic. Vilensky wrote me that "There were a number of stories of encephalitis lethargica patients who lapsed into relatively long-term comas, although not as long as Daysey's. Generally they died but not all did."

Vilensky mentioned a woman named Patricia Maguire, the best known of these, who was called the Sleeping Beauty of Oak Park, Illinois. She lay in a coma for more than five and a half years, and then she died. While she slept, newspaper articles romanticized her condition, often suggesting around holidays that her family sensed she might be waking up. The articles described the devotion of Patricia's mother and sister, who sat by her side for years, hoping, as Daysey's family had hoped, that she would one day wake up. But Patricia Maguire never did.

The neurological and psychiatric after effects of encephalitis lethargic—the physical pathologies, the harrowing "bad behaviors," and even psychoses—were not unique to that disease, and they were tremendously stigmatizing. But it took many decades for doctors to draw a line of causality between encephalitis lethargica and those enduring signs and symptoms.

I can only conclude that Kenneth Appel did not want to label Daysey with a diagnosis that was so damning, so stigmatizing. Daysey had been different from every other encephalitis lethargica patient Kenneth had treated; she had recovered completely. Kenneth spoke of her with awe in his unpublished oral history, but he never wrote a peer-reviewed, clinical case history about her. He characterized her as "a delusional patient" with "schizophrenic symptoms" who, to his surprise, had made a full recovery.

For many decades, according to her memoir, Daysey wondered about her illness, but she found no one who could explain it to her. Her sister and her mother, like Kenneth, simply remained mum. Her suspicion that she might have had a nervous breakdown had been summarily dismissed years earlier by Kenneth, who had said "Oh, no. You had a true organic disease." Kenneth's choice of words seemed to be echoing those of Dr. Thomas Saxty Good's entry in Daysey's Warneford chart: "very grave mischief of an organic character in the brain." Had she but seen that chart, she would also have seen the crucial, clarifying words "encephalitis lethargica." But she never did.

Daysey may eventually have decided to stop trying to find the missing pieces to her personal puzzle. Her illness finally left her alone, and she must simply have decided to reciprocate the gesture.

# Notes

### 1926: Sick

The fear was that the disease was highly contagious ... two people in a single household developed encephalitis lethargica at the same time.

*A Clinical Study of Encephalitis Lethargica (Based on Sixty-Two Cases), British Medical Journal, 1925, June 20, 1120.*

### 1926: Sick

An Austrian neuroscientist, Constantin von Economo, first characterized the disease in 1916 and coined its evocative name.

*The Percipient Observations of Constantin von Economo on Encephalitis Lethargica and Sleep Disruption and Their Lasting Impact on Contemporary Sleep Research, Brain Research Bulletin, 2006, 60:244.*

### 1926: Sick

The rare patient who made a complete recovery

was one who endured just a short acute illness, in the range of two to four months.

*Encephalitis Lethargica Syndrome: 20 New Cases and Evidence of Basal Ganglia Autoimmunity, Brain, 2004, 127:21.*

## 1926: Coma

Dr. Good had presented a paper to the Oxford Medical Society ... in making definitive diagnoses.

*May 9, 1924. The paper was later published in the Journal of Mental Science, 1925, 71: 225-235: Encephalitis Lethargica.*

## 1926: Coma

He was as puzzled as were other doctors ... any more than we can see electricity.

*The History and Progress of Littlemore Hospital, Presidential Address of Thomas Saxty Good, 1930, July 1, 613.*

## 1926: Coma

His recommendation was for bedtime rituals, including recitation of Keats's Ode to Sleep.

*Sleep and Sleeplessness, British Medical Journal, 1925, May 9, 869.*

## 1926: Coma

All of the entries from Daysey's medical records are from the Oxfordshire Health Archives.

## 1938: The Comeback

You cannot see eye to eye with a person you look down upon. We need to be looking eye to eye in psychiatry.

*Comp Psychiatry, 1961, June 2, 129-132. Kenneth E. Appel: Editor's Tribute by Fritz A. Freyhan.*

## 1938: The Comeback

The disease is an infection and not merely a degeneration ... has not been fatal.

*Behavioral Disorders Following Encephalitis: An Experiment in Re-Education. Earl D. Bond and Kenneth E. Appel, 1931, NY, The Commonwealth Fund.*

## 1938: The Comeback

So long as it can be said ... communities.

*Behavioral Disorders Following Encephalitis: An Experiment in Re-Education. Earl D. Bond and Kenneth E. Appel, 1931, NY, The Commonwealth Fund.*

## 1938: The Comeback

A case that taught me a tremendous amount ...

relationship with someone sitting by the bed would be helpful.

*Oral History Interview of Kenneth Appel by Dr. Daniel B. Blain, 1978. The Historical Medical Library of the College of Physicians of Philadelphia. Philadelphia, PA.*

### The Last Thirty Years

I'm leaving in two days to be a housemother at Cardinal Cushing College in Brookline, Mass.

*Cardinal Cushing was a private Catholic women's school that opened in 1952 and closed in 1972.*

### The Last Thirty Years

Back here in Washington I had a brief appearance on TV. The program was called Two Plus You. The reporter was doing a series of Rip Van Winkle stories.

*This was the program that I had stumbled on long before I thought about trying to meet Daysey.*

## Images

Cover. Daysey standing on a cliff in Rockport.
*Permission: The Schlesinger Library, Radcliffe Institute, Harvard University. Rockport Lodge Records.*

Page 11. Daysey and her pipe sometime in the 1970s.
*Permission: Special Collections Research Center, George Washington University.*

Page 23. Daysey's first letter to Miss Burrows.
*From her Oxford University file.*

Page 33. Oxford don with flapping gown riding down a street in Daysey's neighborhood.
*Author photograph, 2009.*

Page 38. Daysey's row house at 2029 37th Street, NW, Georgetown.
*Author photograph, 2009.*

Page 52. The Day family home at 7 Decatur Street in Strasburg, PA. Today the house is the Bachman Funeral Parlor.
*Author photograph, 2008.*

Page 54. Daysey's tombstone.
*Author photograph, 2008.*

Page 58. Tree Day at Wellesley, 1910. Daysey is the second person in the line. From 1914 Wellesley yearbook, *Legenda*.
*Permission: Wellesley College.*

Page 61. Daysey's graduation photograph. From 1914 Wellesley yearbook, *Legenda*.
*Permission: Wellesley College*

Page 64. Final entry in Daysey's Oxford University record.
*From the Oxford University file.*

Page 71. The house at 7 Mansfield Road.
*Author photograph, 2009.*

Page 73. One of the first laboratory reports from the Radcliffe Infirmary.
*From the Warneford Hospital files.*

Page 76. One of the reception petitions for Daysey's admission to the Warneford Hospital.
*From the Warneford Hospital files.*

Page 80. Warneford Psychiatric Hospital.
*Author photograph, 2009.*

Page 96. The chapel at Warneford Psychiatric Hospital.
*Author photograph, 2009.*

Page 107. Final entry in Daysey's medical record from the Warneford Psychiatric Hospital.
*From the Warneford Hospital files.*

Page 110. Passenger list for S.S. George Washington. Marjorie and Marion Day are the seventh and eighth names on the list.
*From www.Ancestry.com*

Page 168. Want ad like the one that caught Daysey's eye.
*From the New York Times, March 21, 1944.*

Page 199. First page of a four-page, hand-written syllabus for Daysey's course Sociology 101.
*From Mount Vernon College archives.*

Page 203. The Rockport Lodge.
*Author photograph, 2009.*

Page 205. Scrapbook entry depicting a winged Daysey leading a hike.
*Permission: The Schlesinger Library, Radcliffe Institute, Harvard University. Rockport Lodge Records.*

Page 207. Daysey cooking bacon and eggs on the rocks at Rockport.
*Permission: The Schlesinger Library, Radcliffe Institute, Harvard University. Rockport Lodge Records.*

Page 212. Flat Rock Point and Thacher's Island lighthouses. *Author photograph, 2009.*

Ruth Levy Guyer

## Acknowledgements

Daysey's friends come first in the long list of people I want to thank for helping me develop this story. My neighbor, Emily Lampert, told me her version of the story in 1977. Even though her account was short and not entirely accurate in every detail, she drew me in with several enchanting anecdotes and set me on a thirty-five year quest to find the complete story. Mimi Harper, Daysey's best friend, provided the "open sesame" for me, giving me Daysey's memoir and also filling in huge blanks in the story. Mimi loved Daysey and conveyed her adoration for her friend in all of the remembrances that she shared with me. She also was extremely generous in linking me to others who knew and loved Daysey and in welcoming me to her Rockport home (which was once Daysey's summer home). Daysey's neighbors in Rockport, David and Enid Wise, and her colleague at Mount Vernon, Jane Highsaw, shared their remembrances of Daysey with me as well. Cathryn Lampert, Emily's daughter, described Daysey to me as a true original, a real intellectual, and a presence who was always younger than her chronological age. At age four, Cathryn was often given the choice by her mother of going to a dorm with a student babysitter while her mother finished teaching her math classes or sitting in someone else's classroom. She typically chose to sit in Daysey's class room, because Daysey was so charismatic.

I received crucial assistance from a number of librarians and archivists. Elizabeth Boardman, the Oxfordshire medical archivist, spent months searching for Daysey's medical files at the Warneford Psychiatric Hospital. Elizabeth also connected me to the archivist at St. Anne's College, David Smith, who sent me Daysey's university file, which contained letters and other records. Elizabeth's colleague, Roy Overall, also corresponded with me about the medical records.

Wilma Slaight at Wellesley College provided key records from Wellesley, including Daysey's transcript, yearbook information, and her masters thesis. She also took the time to go through more than seventy-five years of alumnae magazines to find Daysey's entries in the notes of the class of 1914. Ashley Locke at

George Washington University located syllabi, yearbooks that had pictures of Daysey, and other materials from the Mount Vernon College archives. Pam Kaplan at the Dana Hall schools found records of Daysey's time teaching there, as did Susanna Morikawa at the Mary Lyon School, and Priscilla Jackson at the Ethel Walker School.

I corresponded for several years with Kathryn Allamong Jacobs, Curator of Manuscripts at the Schlesinger Library of the Radcliffe Institute for Advanced Study, about the Rockport Lodge archives. Finally, in the summer of 2011, she wrote that the archives had been catalogued and were available to me. She also told me about the burly workman at the Rockport Lodge who told her that "women in long white gowns" had appeared in the night when he and several other workmen were loading boxes from the Lodge into his truck to take to the dump. The men sensed that the women were very angry, and so they turned around and took the boxes back into the Lodge, thus preserving all of the Lodge's records.

Dora Wong at Haverford College helped me with many aspects of my research during the years when I was teaching at the college and was always enthusiastic about the story. Ann Upton, also at Haverford College, gave me advice on how to find ship records, which helped me track the comings and goings of the Day family in the years when Daysey was in England. Martina Darragh at the National Reference Center for Bioethics Literature helped me find needed materials all through my years of research and always was eager to talk about Daysey.

I spoke to town librarians in many cities where Daysey lived during her years of recovery, and I am grateful for their attempts to track down records of Daysey's years in their towns. All were generous with their time. I also spoke with people involved with the Strasburg Historical Society and with other residents of Strasburg, who shared their recollections with me.

Sarah Sorkin and Libby Mosier, two wonderful writers and two wonderful friends, remained steadfast in their enthusiasm for Daysey's story, always listened carefully as I told them details (and remembered them!), and always had valuable suggestions for how I might best shape the story. I am grateful also for the feedback and enthusiasm and ideas from Lynn Caporale, Betty Cohen, David Everett, Deborah Grosvenor, Anya Guyer, Dana Guyer, Mark Guyer, Sarah Lazin, Bill Loizeaux, Kate Losman, Graciela Michelotti, Jane Reece, Elsa Silverman,

Raisa Williams, the members of the Cornwall Manor book club, and the members of The Salon.

Some months before I saw Daysey's definitive diagnosis in her medical and university records, I suspected what might have made her sick and wrote to Oliver Sacks and Joel Vilensky to ask if they agreed with my conclusion. I am grateful that both were willing to discuss the diagnosis with me.

## About the Author

Ruth Levy Guyer is an American author and commentator. Her essays, articles, reviews, commentaries and stories on medical ethics, environmental ethics, public health, and infectious diseases have appeared in popular and professional journals and magazines, books, and newspapers; her commentaries on wide-ranging topics were a regular feature of NPR's weekend show *All Things Considered* for several years. Her first book, *Baby at Risk: The Uncertain Legacies of Medical Miracles for Babies, Families and Society* (2006) was described by writer/surgeon Richard Selzer as "a brilliant treatment of the conflicted emotions that come into play when a fragile infant comes into the world. ... Surely, it is the best work of its kind."

Guyer has taught courses in bioethics, medical ethics, infectious diseases, writing, AIDS, and environmental ethics for undergraduates at Haverford College, for graduate students at Johns Hopkins University, and for doctors and medical researchers at UCLA and the National Institutes of Health. She received a B.A. in biology from Bryn Mawr College and a Ph.D. in immunology from the University of California, Berkeley. Links to her writing can be found at: www.RuthLevyGuyer.net.